GRADE 2

CW00407657

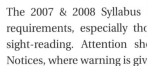

The 2007 & 2008 Syllabus requirements, especially th... sight-reading. Attention sh... Notices, where warning is giv...

The syllabus is obtainable online at www.abrsm.org, from music retailers or from the Services Department, The Associated Board of the Royal Schools of Music, 24 Portland Place, London W1B 1LU, United Kingdom (please send a stamped addressed C5 (162mm x 229mm) envelope).

In exam centres outside the UK, information and syllabuses may be obtained from the Local Representative.

CONTENTS

Where appropriate, pieces in this volume have been checked with original source material and edited as necessary for instructional purposes. Fingering, phrasing, pedalling, metronome marks and the editorial realization of ornaments (where given) are for guidance only; they are not comprehensive or obligatory.

Editor for the Associated Board: **Richard Jones**

DO NOT PHOTOCOPY © MUSIC

Alternative pieces for this grade

Music origination by Barnes Music Engraving Ltd
Cover by Økvik Design
Printed in England by Headley Brothers Ltd,
The Invicta Press, Ashford, Kent

Allegro
Fourth movement from Sonata in G, Hob. XVI/8

Edited by
Howard Ferguson

HAYDN

Like most of Haydn's early keyboard music, the Sonata in G, Hob. XVI/8, from which this Allegro is drawn, was probably written for teaching purposes some time before he entered the service of Prince Esterházy in 1761. In this cheerful movement, the quavers might be lightly detached. The repeated middle phrase (bb. 9–12, 13–16) invites a crescendo up to the third bar, beat 1, followed by a corresponding diminuendo. The fifth RH note in bb. 12 and 16 is a semiquaver (without a rest) in the source. The printed dynamics are editorial suggestions only.

Source: *Divertimento da Cembalo Del Sigre Giuseppe Haÿden* (MS, 1770), Staatsbibliothek zu Berlin, Preussischer Kulturbesitz, Mus.ms.10114

Balletto

LÖHLEIN

Allegretto [♩ = *c*.96]

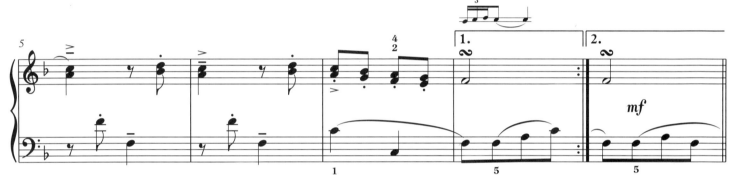

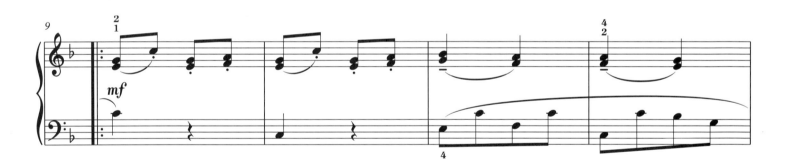

Georg Simon Löhlein (1725–81) was a German composer who studied at the universities of Jena and Leipzig. Later he taught music at Leipzig and, on the basis of this experience, published a keyboard method, the *Clavier-Schule* of 1765, which was widely used in the late 18th and early 19th centuries.

Bourrée

L. MOZART

Leopold Mozart (1719–87) was appointed a violinist to the Salzburg court in 1743 and had become Vice-Kapellmeister by 1763. He established a reputation as a violin teacher, and in 1756 published his famous treatise on violin playing. From about 1760 he spent much time on the musical education of his two exceptionally gifted children, Maria Anna ('Nannerl') and Wolfgang Amadeus, who had been born in 1751 and 1756 respectively. Leopold's small keyboard pieces, such as this Bourrée, were written with this purpose in mind.

© Copyright 2002 by Editio Bärenreiter Praha
Reproduced by permission. All enquiries for this piece apart from the exams should be addressed to Bärenreiter Ltd, Burnt Mill, Elizabeth Way, Harlow, Essex, CM20 2HX.

Grandmother's Tales

from *Spring Morning*

B:1

SARAUER

This piece is by the Czech composer Alois Sarauer (1901–80).

AB 3144

B:2

Der Kuckuck und die Nachtigall

from *Kinderalbum*, Op. 55

KRUG

Der Kuckuck und die Nachtigall The Cuckoo and the Nightingale; **Kinderalbum** Children's Album

The German pianist and composer Arnold Krug (1849–1904) studied with Gurlitt and at the Leipzig Conservatory. He taught at the Stern Conservatory in Berlin, and later returned to his native city Hamburg as a music teacher, choirmaster and conductor. In this piece the LH accompaniment may be articulated like the RH melody, except in bb. 13–14, where the LH takes over the melody, implying legato, and the RH has staccato accompanying chords. The RH slur in b. 12 has been added by the editor, by analogy with the one in b. 10.

Source: *Kinderalbum*, Op. 55 (London: Augener, 1896)

Die Nachtigall

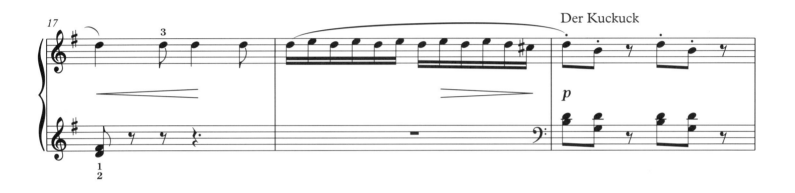

Der Kuckuck

The Bee

from *Fantasy Studies*, Op. 13

ROWLEY

Allegretto ♩. = 72

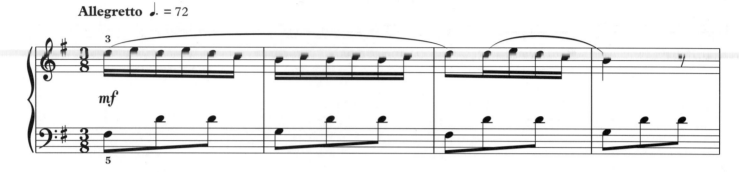

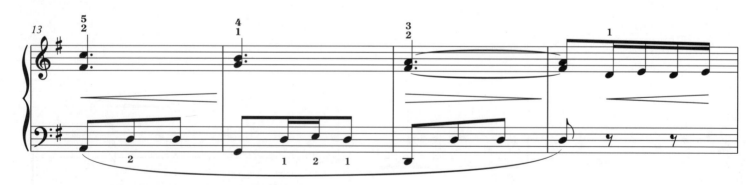

The English composer Alec Rowley (1892–1958) studied at the Royal Academy of Music, and in 1919 became professor at Trinity College of Music. He wrote a great deal of music for educational purposes. In this piece, the editor has added the RH slur in bb. 7–8 and has changed the RH *f* ♯ in b. 16 from a crotchet to a quaver. A suitable tempo for 'The Bee' in the exam would be ♩. = *c*.63.

Source: *Fantasy Studies for the Second Year*, Op. 13 (London: W. Rogers, 1917)

for Joel

The Temple by the Sea

JOHN McLEOD

Slowly and peacefully ♩ = *c.*65

The Scottish composer John McLeod (b. 1934) studied with Lennox Berkeley at the Royal Academy of Music. The occasion of this piece is recorded in the words 'Remembering Bali…12 October 2002'. The composer has written: 'Perched on a small island just off the southern coast of Bali, there is a temple called Tanah Lot. Its shape becomes a dark silhouette as the sun sets and the ghostly spirits of ancient gods return. This piece is based on the notes of some distant gamelan music (A C♯ D E G♯) which I heard as I stood beside this mysterious place.'

Reproduced from *Spectrum 4: An International Collection of 66 Miniatures for Solo Piano* (ABRSM Publishing)

Close to Danger

from *Piano Pageant*, Book 3

C:2

DONALD WAXMAN

Donald Waxman (b. 1925) is a native of Baltimore. He began his musical training at the Peabody Conservatory, studying piano, cello and composition, the latter with Elliott Carter. He later studied at the Julliard School. He has composed in many genres, and is well known in the field of piano pedagogy.

Garage Sale

from *Really Easy Jazzin' About*

PAM WEDGWOOD

Pam Wedgwood (b. 1947) is recognized around the world as one of the UK's most prolific and successful composers of popular repertoire for young instrumentalists. About 'Garage Sale', she has written: 'You can use a heavy rock rhythm with this piece.' It is drawn from *Really Easy Jazzin' About: Fun Pieces for Piano/Keyboard*, which belongs to a large series aimed at introducing jazz and other popular styles to elementary players of the piano and other instruments.

COMBAT PR

B-17G FI
FORTRESS
in World War 2

COMBAT PROFILE:
B-17G FLYING FORTRESS
in World War 2

ROGER A. FREEMAN

LONDON
IAN ALLAN LTD

Acknowledgements

The author wishes to record his appreciation for information and material provided by the veterans of the bomber crew who undertook the combat sortie described in this publication. They are: Charles Beard, Roger Dearmon, Robert Doherty, Charles Haywood, Paul Herring, Luigi Iacoviello, Everett Johnson, John Wilson and William Wood. My sincere thanks are also extended to Robert Apperson, Arthur Crocker, Steve Birdsall, Bruce Robertson, Geoffrey Ward, Jean Freeman, William Rinehart and George Pennick for their help; and last but far from least Norman Ottaway for his excellent drawings.

Note: The illustrations in Chapter 1 — Combat Sortie, include photographs taken on the day and operation covered but the majority are purely representative of what is described.

Sole distributors for the USA

Osceola, Wisconsin 54020, USA

First published 1990

ISBN 0 7110 1921 5

Published by Ian Allan Ltd, Shepperton, Surrey; and printed by Ian Allan Printing Ltd at their works at Coombelands in Runnymede, England

Contents

Front cover photography by Richard E. Bagg

Previous page:
The ultimate Flying Fortress: gear starting to lower, a late production B-17G prepares to land. The defensive armament shows well in this photograph.
H. Holmes

Below:
The leadship of 96th 'B' Group, flown by Capt Litowitz on the mission described. Officially B-17G 42-31053, BX:W of 338th Bomb Squadron, it was nicknamed *Stingy* **at the request of Maj-Gen Fred Anderson, when head of VIII Bomber Command, for his small son.**

Introduction

That the Flying Fortress has become the most famous name among US military aircraft is largely due to two factors; initially through the attentions of the American news media and subsequently as epitomising the tool of trade for World War 2 bomber crews battling through fierce opposition to reach their objective. The origin of the name for Boeing's Model 299 was the caption by-line of a newspaper man following the first public display of the aircraft at Boeing's Seattle factory on 16 July 1935. Although a typical example of media exaggeration — for even by 1935 standards the aircraft's potential defensive armament of five hand-held machine guns was only modest — it was a description that Boeing, anxious to attract a production order, was quick to exploit. Flying Fortress became a registered Boeing name, eventually to be presented on a nameplate attached to the instrument panel of several thousand of its kind.

The US Army Air Corps (USAAC) preferred designations to names for its aircraft and when 13 Model 299s were ordered for trial purposes they were known as YB-17s — Y for evaluation. B for bomber and 17 for the seventeenth bomber design accepted by the USAAC. The four-engined, all-metal monoplane was certainly an advanced bomber design as far as USAAC leaders were concerned and they were eager to procure more. But the US government's stance at that time was one of isolationism and a long range bomber was not conducive to promoting such policy and, unconvinced by the assurance that the big bomber was required for coastal defence — attacking a seaborne enemy force — there was no follow-up order. The bomber enthusiasts of the USAAC saw in the B-17 the potential means of achieving their long nurtured desire to create a strategic bombing force, believing that this was the way of

establishing air power in its own right. In lobbying for funds for more of these expensive bombers the USAAC did not mention the prevailing political implications. They did, however, afford the B-17 a 'good press' at every opportunity through record-breaking long-distance flights and other exploits.

Development of the B-17 centred on high altitude operation where, in the late 1930s it appeared that the aircraft could fly high enough to avoid antiaircraft artillery and was fast enough to outrun interceptors. High altitude operation was made possible by the fitting of turbo superchargers to the engines and this, plus an advanced crew oxygen supply and the installing of data computing bombsight, gave some credence to the visionaries' beliefs.

Only a change in the political scene, by President Roosevelt's appreciation that the United States would ultimately become involved in a war threatening to engulf Europe, brought the first order for a service production model of the Flying Fortress, the turbo-equipped B-17B which was delivered to the USAAC shortly after the outbreak of hostilities in Europe. The 39 B-17Bs were followed by 38 B-17C and 42 B-17D models, incorporating further refinements of the original design, mostly in armament, and giving a creditable 323mph top speed at 25,000ft. Twenty of the B-17Cs were sent to the RAF in 1941 and used by Bomber Command in experimental daylight raids. The RAF planned to use these aircraft at as high an altitude as possible on single sorties. In the event, the desired 32,000ft could rarely be attained and some of the aircraft — Fortress Is in RAF terminology — fell victim to the Luftwaffe.

Meanwhile, having appreciated some of the Fortress's deficiencies, Boeing undertook a radical re-design and came up with the B-17E introducing the distinctive large curved tail fin and

much improved armament. After 512 B-17Es, the similar B-17F — considered the first truly battle-worthy Fortress — entered service in the summer of 1942. A total of 3,405 B-17Fs were built and this became the principal model involved in the US 8th Air Force's unescorted daylight raids into Germany and Occupied Europe during 1943. The B-17G, distinguished by its 'chin' turret, was the ultimate production model and the most numerous, a total of 8,680 being built and at peak inventory they equipped 108 squadrons of the 8th Air Force in England and 20 of the 15th Air Force in Italy. Some 200 B-17E/F/G Fortresses were used by the RAF, principally on maritime reconnaissance and electronic countermeasures duties, while the US Navy and Coast Guard operated a small number. Also, six were supplied to Canada in 1943 for use as transatlantic mailplanes.

The main Fortress units were those of the 8th and 15th Air Forces that, together with B-24 Liberator complements, carried out a strategic bombing campaign against Nazi Germany's war economy, bombing manufacturing industry and power sources. At times both forces were diverted to tactical operations in more direct support of ground forces. Most of the aircraft's forays into hostile airspace were fiercely contested by the enemy defences and at times they were under fire for hours. The basically good design and construction played a large part in enabling many Fortresses to return from operations with heavy damage which other aircraft types could not have sustained and remained airborne. The rugged reputation of the B-17 may have been exaggerated but it was certainly justified. Interestingly of all World War 2 bomber aircraft, more B-17s were utilised for civil use in postwar years than any other type, primarily because of its reliability and good handling qualities.

Combat Sortie

During World War 2 the United States Army Air Forces undertook a strategic bombing offensive against its enemies' war industries, military facilities and power sources. The campaign was waged in daylight at the edge of the stratosphere and with intended precision. Most of these aerial forays were fiercely contested and as the scale of operations grew, the battles that resulted can justly be called epic.

To give an idea of the scale of activity that these operations engendered, the details of the preparation and participation of a single Fortress on a particular day's operation is detailed. In this reconstruction of an actual mission involving a B-17G Fortress flying from England to attack a target in central Germany in February 1944, it should be appreciated that daily these tasks were being repeated a hundredfold at dozens of different locations. While there were developments in procedures, technique and equipment during the 1942-45 period of the campaign, there were no major changes in the way a mission was organised. The actions and tasks in the preparation and execution of the sortie described are typical.

MSgt Floyd Franklin opens the door of a shack and steps out into the chill of the English night. Rubbing the sleep from his eyes he tries to find some distinction in the blackness before him. Presently, as his pupils adjust, a slight lightening silhouettes the familar outline of his charge, Boeing B-17 '988'. Propeller blades, the hump of engine nacelles and fuselage, the distinctive sweep of the ventral stabiliser impose above the black skyline of woods and hedgerows. Reaching inside his sheepskin jacket, Chief, as he is familiarly called, retrieves a flashlight clipped to his coverall pocket, to shine on his wristwatch. It is nearly 4am, only four-and-a-half hours since he had rolled, exhausted, on to the improvised bed in the shack and fallen asleep almost instantly. Across the airfield he can hear trucks on the move; no doubt the ordnance crews collecting bombs from the dump. From over the adjoining fields comes the labouring chuffing of a steam locomotive hauling through nearby Eccles Road railway station on the line skirting the southern boundary of Snetterton Heath airfield.

Blowing on his hands for warmth, Chief pushes open the door and goes back into the shack. The flashlight picks out a sleeping figure covered by army topcoats. His hand on the shoulder brings Cpl Tom Brownie, the armourer, out of his slumbers. 'Just on four. Ordnance is on the move', is the gentle opener from the Chief as he switches on an improvised table light powered by cycle batteries. Brownie makes no reply but after a few seconds swings his boot-clad feet down on to the concrete slab floor and sits on the edge of the bed while reaching for a Thermos flask. After pouring out coffee into three tin mugs he hands one to the Chief, saying, 'Will you start the putt-putt and check

Below:
The armourer fixes the chin turret guns while another member of the ground crew prepares to start the putt-putt.

the bay for me?'. 'Sure', replies the Chief. The putt-putt is the popular phonetic name for the auxiliary power plant, a small petrol engine-powered generator used to boost the electrical supply in the aircraft, a necessity if the batteries are not to be depleted while the various systems are tested before the aircraft's engines are running to generate its own electrical power.

By now the third occupant of the shack has awakened and stretches with an oath; 'Jeepers fellers, let a guy sleep won't you'. Corporal Robert G. Apperson, mechanic, taking his morning shift on '988', is handed a mug of coffee by the Chief who gives the message: 'Engine start, 0805'. This is the time when engines will be started on their bomber for the mission it has to undertake

today; before then there is much work to do. Brownie lights a cigarette. There is little conversation as each man comes to terms with his awakening and the chill of the night. It is cold enough for breath to show in the dim light, for the shack affords little isolation from the external elements. The ground crew had made this shelter from salvaged wood packing cases employing only basic carpentry. Depite the chill, drowsiness is not easily shed; all three men have had little sleep of late. They had been alerted the previous evening that their bomber was to be ready to undertake another mission the following morning; all had worked long into the night to carry out the necessary maintenance on the Fortress which had just returned from a mission deep into Germany.

A vehicle drives on to the hardstanding, its screened lights playing across the large wheels of the B-17 as it swings round and comes to a halt under the bomber's wingtip. A man jumps out and runs to the tent. The face of the Squadron Armament Officer appears round the edge of the door; 'Ten M-43!' He grins and is gone. The Jeep departs into the darkness as Brownie extinguishes his cigarette and mumbles: 'Same load as yesterday'. He gets up and leaves the shack, followed by the Chief.

The Chief pulls the protective cover from the auxiliary engine-generator, picks up the attached cable and walks over to the aircraft. He shines his flashlight along the left underside of the fuselage below the cockpit until he finds a small door. Unlatching this he plugs in the power cable from the putt-putt. Meanwhile Brownie, also using a torch, has gone to the door on the left-hand side of the Fortress's fuselage. He opens it and, with a hand each side, pulls himself up into the blackness of the fuselage. Unclipping his flashlight from his top coverall pocket, Brownie first turns its beam left along towards the tailwheel well and the tail gun position. There is no purpose in this act, just a habit he has formed in countless similar entries into the darkened interior of B-17s over the past few months. Closing the door behind him, the armourer moves forward up the fuselage, past the two waist window-gun positions and round the gimbal supporting the under-turret, known as 'the ball'. A bulkhead door leads into the radio operator's compartment and beyond, another door to the bomb-bay. Brownie carefully sidles along the narrow bomb-bay catwalk, being careful not to catch his sheepskin jacket on the racks. The bulkhead door at the far end of the bomb-bay has been left open and Brownie steps up on to the engineer's compartment, squeezes by the top turret base frame and drops down through the opening in the flightdeck behind the two pilots' seats. Stooping, he enters the nose compartment, dodges round the navigator's seat and table on the left side

and finally reaches his goal, the bombardier's seat in the nose.

By now the Chief has the putt-putt started and running smoothly. Brownie switches on the lights which illuminate the bombardier's panel attached to the left side of the nose between the forward observation window. Down below the front of the panel are two levers, one so shaped that it prevents the other being moved first. Brownie pushes this control lever rearwards and immediately the whirr of electric motors can be heard as the bomb doors come down and open out. When the two doors are fully down a red light illuminates on the bombardier's panel. Brownie then moves the other lever to one of its three positions marked 'Selective'. This is the bomb control lever and in this position it allows selective drop of bombs from the racks. He then turns on the Intervelometer on the panel, which determines the set intervals at which bombs can be dropped in train. The bomb shackles and electric firing solenoids are still fixed to the racks for the previous day's mission and the armourer sets up various release combinations of the panel switches and tests them by pressing the bomb release attached to the top of the panel. Various lights, white, red and amber, flash on

and off. Satisfied, he cuts the switches and pushes the bomb control lever forward through to the 'Salvo' – the emergency drop of all bombs together – and then brings it back to the 'Lock' position.

Meanwhile, the Chief is standing under the bomb-bay watching the operation of the bomb shackles in the aircraft's soft interior lighting. Satisfied all are operating correctly, he pulls himself up on to the catwalk and goes forward into the cockpit. Sliding the left pilot's side window, the Chief reaches out and pulls away the canvas cover which has been laid over the top of the cockpit to keep frost from clouding the windshield. He lets the canvas fall to the ground and, after closing the side window, exchanges a few comments with Brownie, who has left the nose compartment and is making his way back to the bomb-bay.

Below:
Ordnance crew direct the edging back of a bomb trailer under the bomb bay in the darkness at Snetterton Heath.

Bottom:
A 500-pounder being raised by cable winch into the bay. Note the stainless steel shackle attached to the two lugs.

Bob Apperson, the duty mechanic, has emerged from the tent and, using a wooden stepladder, proceeds to remove the canvas wraps over each engine cowling. He has just moved the steps under another engine when the lights of a motor vehicle come stabbing through the darkness towards the aircraft: ordnance crews and bomb load have arrived. With much flashing of torches and shouted directions the rearmost of the bomb trailers is disconnected from the bomb service truck and manhandled under the nose of the Fortress, being carefully guided back under the bomb-bay. The lights in the bomb-bay show the tricycle configured trailer to have 10 M-43 500lb General Purpose bombs. Each has a single yellow band painted round the front and another round the rear, indicating a TNT filling. The ordnance men remove the stainless steel shackles from the aircraft's racks and attach them to the two lugs on each bomb. A cable attached via pulleys to a hand winch in the bomber is pulled down and slipped round a bomb and secured. The bomb is then carefully winched up into the bay until it is at the required station on the rack. Once the shackle has been fixed to the rack the cable is removed from the bomb and the same procedure repeated until all 10 bombs on the trolley have been placed in the bay. While this work is in progress the Chief has been keeping a close eye on proceedings to see that nothing in the bay is damaged; the loading crew works fast and with the haste a bomb can accidentally be swung against some piece of equipment. The Chief knows if this should happen the heavy bomb usually wins.

The empty trolley is pushed clear and attached again to the Chevrolet bomb service truck. While this is done, one member of the ordnance crew climbs up into the bay to screw on the bomb fins, kicking them tight. Finally nose and tail fuses are carefully screwed into the bombs. Each fuse has a small arming propeller-like vane which turns to arm the fuse as the bomb drops. The vane is made safe by a securing wire which will be removed by a member of the air crew after the bomber has taken off for its target. The whole bomb loading operation has taken 35min. It is an exacting task but the ordnance crew have learned to work in an ordered and quick way.

Once the bomb service truck has departed, the ground crew can begin pre-flighting the bomber. The Chief and his assistant begin by pulling on the lowest propeller blade of No 1 engine, that on the far left as viewed from the pilot's cockpit. It is pulled through nine blades so that the propeller makes three complete revolutions, an action to remove any fuel that has accumulated in the engine cylinders overnight. In this laborious task the armourer comes to lend a hand. While they are 'pulling through the fans' another truck arrives. The driver carefully reverses up close to the rear fuselage door and 10 wooden boxes of .50in calibre ammunition are unloaded by the light of a lamp fixed inside the covered rear of the vehicle. There is an enforced blackout in the United Kingdom to avoid attracting the attention of enemy aircraft. However, unless there is an air raid warning in progress the lights are not extinguished by those working around the airfield. Brownie goes over to help, climbing up into the fuselage to stack each box of ammunition as it is handed up by the two ordnance men. The armourer prefers to receive the ammunition before the bombs are loaded so that the rounds for

Above:
A flashlight is handed up for another check on No 3 engine.

the front end guns can go in through the open bomb-bay doors. Now it will be necessary for each box to be carried forward, an awkward task. The Chief, on his way to the cockpit, takes the rope handle on the end of an ammunition box and helps Brownie lug one forward. Apperson also comes to give a hand.

In the cockpit, the Chief takes the right seat – the co-pilot's – to commence his engine checks by turning on the battery and ignition switches. Apperson having the putt-putt running again, has picked up a fire extinguisher and moved out to stand in front of No 3 engine – the left inner – where he can flash his torch to indicate his position to the Chief. The Chief, bending over to look under the pilot's seats, is making sure that the terminals on the voltage converters are not short-circuited as sometimes spent ammunition cases can find their way there. The fuel booster pumps are turned on while the pressure reading is checked and the throttle set at the 1,000rpm mark. He then sets the hand primer of No 1 engine and operates the priming pump on the right side of the cockpit, giving long steady strokes to atomise fuel as he holds down the appropriate starter switch for 12sec to build up sufficient inertia. Using the same hand, he slips his thumb on to the mesh switch which engages the electrical starter with the engine. No 1 seems to protest and then, with a flash of exhaust flames, catches and splutters into life. Chief moves the mixture control lever on the central pedestal to 'Auto Rich' and turns his gaze to the oil pressure gauge, watching the indicator slowly rising. The engine having smoothed out, the Chief stops priming. When the oil pressure shows 70lb, the Chief turns his attention to starting the other three

Below:
The last of the load is secured. Bombs are shackled to both central and both outer vertical racks. The screwed rods which open and close the bay doors can be seen at the bottom of the photograph.

engines by similar procedure. Only No 3 proves difficult, as always, requiring three attempts. But why this happens is a mystery as everything has been frequently checked and found in order. When all engines have been running smoothly for a few minutes whilst the instruments are checked for correct readings, the Chief then runs up each individually to check magneto delivery and after this, if satisfactory, the turbo-superchargers are tested. Then each propeller pitch mechanism is varied before being finally satisfied that all is performing to the stipulated requirements. Fuel and ignition switches are cut and all engines shut down. The engine run-ups have taken nearly 15min.

A clipboard that has been lodged behind the pilot's windshield is picked up by the Chief to study the Form 1A thereon, recording the pilots' complaints of mechanical problems encountered on the previous day's flight. A slight tail-wheel shimmy was reported on landing and the flight engineer also reported vibration in the top turret rotating mechanism. There had been no prior opportunity to check these as the first essential had been to service the bomber for another mission. The Chief hauls himself out of the co-pilot's seat and goes down into the nose, opens the hatch, grasps the edge and swings down to the ground some six feet below. He calls out to the armourer, who is standing on a stepladder examining the chin turret: 'Brownie, did you check out the top turret?'. 'Yeah' comes the reply, 'looked at it last night. Seemed plenty free; but I cleaned the ring gear and gave it a little oil.'

The Chief, checking his Form 1A, stoops under the fuselage and goes back to the rear door, pulls himself up into the aircraft and starts to examine the tail-wheel oleo. Producing a pocket rule he measures between the oleo attaching pins, then shines his torch down on the tail-wheel yoke. At this moment Apperson looks up through the tail-wheel well. 'Found the trouble?' he enquires. 'Yeah, the shear bolt's bust. That's why he was getting shimmy. Never took the lock off quick enough after landing. You'll have to give me a hand.' While the two mechanics go about inserting another aluminium shear bolt in the tail-wheel castor assembly, another truck has arrived on '988's' dispersal point. A soldier in the back jumps out, lets down the tail gate and carries body armour into the shack. This is worn by the fliers, having been proved quite effective in stopping low velocity splinters from bursting anti-aircraft shells. He then removes a .50in calibre machine gun and carries that into the shack. Three more guns follow. These are the weapons used by the bombardier and navigator in the front of the aircraft. They have just been collected from the squadron armoury where they have

been cleaned and inspected. Each gun, weighing 64lb, has an average rate of fire of approximately 850 rounds/min with a muzzle velocity — the speed at which a bullet leaves the gun barrel — of 2,850ft/sec. The effective range — that at which destruction can be wrought on an enemy aircraft — is around 3,500ft. The USAAF standardised on this weapon, the half-inch diameter bullets being judged to have far more destructive effect than the rifle-calibre machine guns standard on British and German bombers.

The Dodge truck bringing the armament departs, while Brownie prepares to install the four nose guns. The other .50s will be collected by the air gunners themselves and fixed into position when they arrive. As soon as Apperson is ready to lend a hand, one gun at a time is removed from the shack where they have been placed to give weather protection and, using the stepladder, the 'chin turret' guns are installed. This armament is remotely controlled and sighted by the bombardier in the nose. The turret has been turned to the extreme right so that its rear is easily accessible. Brownie slides each of the two guns into their mounts and the perforated blast barrels before securing them. The guns had not been fired on yesterday's mission and the two magazines, each with 365 rounds, are full. The ammunition trace is fed into the guns and the charging levers set.

While the armourer goes back into the bomber via the nose hatch, Apperson retrieves two more guns from the shack and hands them up. These are installed in the two 'cheek' positions in the nose side windows for use by the navigator. The positions are staggered, that on the left side being placed further forward than that on the right in order to clear the navigator's work area. As a consequence this gun has a more restricted field of fire. With the restricted visibility

at these stations they are of limited value in forward defence. The small wooden ammunition boxes under each gun still have the 132 rounds loaded the previous day. The ammunition trace is pulled up to each gun but the weapons are not cocked. For safety this is left for the navigator to carry out once the bomber is airborne.

Yet another vehicle approaches in the darkness. 'Here's the gas wagon', Brownie calls out. Apperson answers with 'Okay' from the tent where he has gone to fortify himself with more coffee from a large Thermos flask — appropriated from a wrecked B-17 which had been cannibalised for spare parts.

Although the B-17 tanks were refilled after yesterday's mission, the ground crew's engine tests have consumed several gallons. The early morning visit of the gas wagon was to top up the tanks. The B-17G has a maximum total fuel tankage capacity of 2,780US gal and while a good reserve is always allowed in computing mission fuel requirements, it was standard policy to fill the tanks to the maximum to cover any emergency. Today's mission stipulates not less than 2,400gal but the tanks will still be filled to the brim.

With the aid of a torch Apperson signals the large articulated fuel truck back to a position in front of the nose. While the gas crews remove the hoses from the rear of the tanker, Apperson goes back into the aircraft to check that the static electricity safety wire is grounded. He then pulls himself up out of the hatch in the radio room roof, having previously removed the cover,

Below:
Topping the tanks. The gas wagon operator watches for the 'cut' signal from the ground crew man on the wing. The extensions fixed to the chin turret gun barrels are to prevent heat and chemical scoring of the Plexiglas when the guns were fired in full up elevation.

and edges forward along the top of the fuselage until he can slide down on to the left wing.

The gas crew hand up the filler hose over the leading edge of the wing between the two engines where it can reach all five filling points. There is a strict sequence for topping up to avoid overflow of the tanks nearer the fuselage due to the dihedral of the wing. From experience Apperson knows that the engine run-ups will have used between 50 and 80gal and that it will be only necessary to check and top up the cells in the outer wing sections which gravity feed the main tanks. These 18 small cells, nine in each wing squeezed between the ribs, were not part of the original B-17 design but are a later addition with the object of extending combat range. Made of a rubber composition with self-sealing qualities, they are known as the Tokyo tanks, a term derived from the saying that they would 'get a B-17 to Tokyo'. There are two access doors covering two filler caps for the Tokyo tanks in the left wing and Apperson first undoes the innermost, puts in the hose nozzle and signals the gas pump operator. After topping up, the cap is replaced and tightened before moving to the outer filler. Topping up completed, the hose is handed down while Apperson again checks that he has secured the filler caps. Leaking fuel from an unsecured filler point might be ignited by engine exhaust. Meanwhile the Chief has been out on the other wing,

carrying out similar tank topping, the gas wagon having two independent supply hoses.

With hoses re-coiled and stored, the gas wagon disappears into the gloom to top up another B-17. Gas crews on a bomber station are busy men, hauling around 70,000gal of aviation spirit for each mission. One tanker holds 4,000gal so it is usually necessary to make a separate journey to replenish each B-17 after a major mission. The two fuel dumps at Snetterton Heath hold a total of 144,000gal and are constantly replenished by a fleet of British 'Pool' petrol road tankers from rail tanks at a nearby station.

A lightening of the sky in the east heralds dawn. The Chief walks round the main wheels of the bomber and examines the 56in-diameter tyres for damage. He had inspected them the previous afternoon but another going over is all part of his routine. On take-off the B-17 will be grossing near 35 tons and a tyre failure could be catastrophic. In fact, the Chief double checks everything. He knows that the crew face dangers enough without the hazard of mechanical or equipment failures that might be due to slackness on the part of the ground crew. Satisfied with the landing gear he then moves under the

Below:
The approach of dawn lightens the English countryside as the crew chief pre-flights the bomber.

engines, shining his flashlight on to the oil-stained concrete below. Wright Cyclone engines have an oily reputation due to the extreme low temperatures at high altitude causing oil to be thrown from crankcase breathers and collecting within the cowlings. The Chief keeps an eye open to see that this waste is not excessive and the clues are to be found on the ground under the engines after they have been run up. He pushes the tubular engine inspection frame across the hardstand, climbs up and has a look inside the cowl of No 3 engine, which gives difficulty in starting. The air cooling vanes on each of the nine cylinders are examined but all seems satisfactory.

Attention is then turned to the exhaust manifold extending back to the turbo-supercharger compressor 'bucket' wheel on the underside of the nacelle. The turbo enables the 1,200hp-rated engine to maintain full power performance at altitudes between 20,000ft and 30,000ft. Exhaust gases turn the bucket wheel which feeds compressed air via an intercooler to the engine carburettors. The Chief runs his flashlight over each engine's turbo bucket wheel and spins them with his hand. These can become red hot in operation and if too much speed is built up they could disintegrate.

In the east the sky continues to lighten. The oxygen team has arrived and are in the Fortress to check that there has been no leakage since the system was replenished after yester-

day's mission. A B-17G has four independent low pressure oxygen systems, each supplying a portion of the crew with the object of reducing the possibility of complete oxygen failure through combat damage. The major supply is contained in 18 light metal bottles, each giving approximately five hours' supply for one man at 30,000ft. Additionally the ball turret has its own supply and there are 10 walk-around bottles at convenient locations with each containing an average of nine minutes' supply. The oxygen man checks that the pressure of 425lb/sq in is available and, finding everything in order, swings out of the nose hatch and goes back to his vehicle. This tows a cart laden with high-pressure cylinders from which aircraft systems can be replenished.

Below:
Station transport: the Dodge 6 × 6 truck ferried ground personnel from the communal and living sites to the airfield.

Bottom:
The crew of *The Iron Ass*. Front, left to right: 1Lt Paul Herring, pilot; Flt Off Charles Beard, co-pilot; 2Lt John Wilson, navigator; and 2Lt William Wood, bombardier. Back row, left to right: TSgt George Goetz, engineer; TSgt Robert Doherty, radio operator; SSgt Luigi Iacoviello, left waist gunner; SSgt Roy Johnson, original ball turret gunner; SSgt Everett Johnson, right waist gunner; and SSgt Charles Haywood, tail gunner.

The Fortress is now ready for war. The gaining daylight reveals that it is one of a dozen dispersed alongside hedgerows and trees. To the southwest a hangar and a number of buildings take shape. The Chief is munching a stale doughnut as he surveys the scene, mulling over the reasons for No 3 engine's reluctance to start. The whole area is comparatively silent, so that the distant chugging of a locomotive on a nearby railway is dominant. Then more trucks are heard and seen proceeding round the perimeter roads. The Chief glances at his watch: 0735hrs, the crews should be on their way. Presently a large 'six by six' truck (a name derived from its 6 × 6 wheel drive) swings up the taxi road to the dispersal point. A man jumps from the cab, runs round and lets down the tail gate. The crew flow out, lugging parachute packs and large olive green flight bags. They wear a mixture of flying clothes: olive coveralls, heavy brown sheepskin jackets and trousers, and one man has a light blue one-piece electrically heated flying suit. Most gather around the rear entrance door of the Fortress and don 'Mae West' water immersion life preservers and parachute harnesses. One man detaches himself from the rest and walks towards the Chief. Unlike the others, he still wears an officer's peaked cap but no badges of rank are visible on his coveralls. This is 1Lt Paul Herring, captain of the crew, a wiry, dark-haired young man of 24. 'Hi Chief, got the Form 1A?' he asks in a confident southern accent. 'Yeah', the Chief responds, handing him the clipboard with the form on which Herring entered those items with which he was unhappy during the previous flight. 'Found the cause of the tail-wheel shimmy. Broken safety bolt', the Chief comments as he looks at the Form 1A with Herring. 'Guess someone was late pulling off the lock when you landed yesterday', he grins. Herring calls to one of the crew who is clipping a parachute harness up between his legs and over his yellow 'Mae West': 'Hey Charlie, the Chief says we broke the tail wheel shear bolt'. Charlie is Flt Off Charles Beard, the co-pilot, a solidly built extrovert of 22 and another Southerner. Coming over to Herring and the Chief he says 'Not me! I was right on the ball.' They have a friendly discussion about the matter and follow the Chief to the tail-wheel assembly as he points out the location of the safety bolt.

'Okay', exclaims Herring, 'better do the ground check.' By this he means the visual outside inspection of the aircraft which a pilot has to perform before entering. It may look haphazard but there is a definite route and order to this. From the rear fuselage entrance door Herring, Beard and the Chief move forward along the right side of the fuselage. Herring glances up at the right waist window where SSgt Luigi Iacoviello is in the process of sliding his .50 into the barrel mount. 'Okay Ike?' 'Sure', comes the reply. The chubby Iacoviello hailing from Massachusetts, is 27 years old. Herring and Beard duck down under the fuselage where SSgt Roger Dearmon is fixing two guns in the ball turret. Dearmon is 24 and his short build makes him a good candidate to ride in the tight confines of the ball. The turret door, which also serves as an armoured back panel for the gunner, is hinged down on the hardstand and Dearmon is kneeling on it reaching into the turret. From Tennessee, he is the newest member of the team, having only recently been assigned to replace a gunner who has been moved to another crew. 'Everything all right Sergeant?' Herring enquires. 'No problem Lieutenant', comes the reply.

The pilots glance at the bomb-bay doors which the armourer has retracted, before passing on to examine the right main landing gear and wheel. There is a brief discussion with the Chief as to how many landings the tyres have seen. Herring looks up into the wheel nacelle, the control cables and electric wiring. He knows the Chief will have double-checked all this already and he doesn't want to be too searching in his inspection so that the Chief does not think he has his confidence. Next Herring and Beard move forward under the turbo, Herring puts up a hand and spins the bucket wheel while Beard looks along the exhaust line and checks the cowling fasteners are tight. They then move to

the outer engine, No 4, before walking along the trailing edge of the wing examining the flaps and aileron and not forgetting to look at the fuel cap doors. Moving to the front of the aircraft both pilots run their eyes over the propellers for nicks or cracks and then move on towards the aircraft's nose. Here Herring checks that the protective cover over the pitot tube has been removed. There had been major accidents caused through this being left in place, preventing air pressure building up in the tube and so giving no indication of airspeed on the cockpit instrument when the aircraft took off. Bombardier 2Lt William Wood is in the nose. Another 24-year-old of athletic build, he was a record-breaking track star at high school. No bomb sight today and Wood will act as a togglier, the popular name for the member of aircrew who toggles (operates the release switch) bombs on the visual sighting of another aircraft's release. Apperson is on the stepladder giving a final polish to the Plexiglas nosepiece: it is imperative that the bombardier's vision is not impaired by a transparency clouded by the effects of the chemical discharge from flare and marker bomb smoke or exhaust from other aircraft engines.

On the right hand side of the nose Herring notices that an 18th yellow bomb symbol has been added to the outline indicating missions completed. 'Still haven't got anyone to paint the name on for us?' he asks the Chief. 'Guy I asked in the paint shop hasn't turned up yet. I'll give him another reminder', he is told. Most of the B-17s on the airfield have nicknames emblazoned on their noses and the Herring crew have chosen *The Iron Ass* for this bomber which they are assigned to fly. This name is a play on words, an ass being the American derivation of the British 'arse', with an iron ass meaning someone who is tough, insensitive.

Through the left hand nose side window navigator 2Lt John Wilson can be seen bent over his table. He is a slim 23-year-old hailing from California. Wilson is the humorist of the crew, a great practical joker.

Continuing their inspection, the pilots proceed along the front, scanning the props and engines of the left wing before moving round under its tip and along the trailing edge, examining the flight surfaces. They then look at the engine nacelles and landing gear on that side. Out from under the trailing edge and along the left side of the fuselage towards the tail. This B-17 has only been in service a few weeks but already the matt olive paintwork on the upper surfaces is stained. Painted in light grey on the fuselage, just above the wing trailing edge, are the large letters 'QJ', and aft of the waist gun position a similarly sized letter 'A'. The 'QJ' identifies the 339th Bombardment Squadron and the 'A' is the individual aircraft

letter within that squadron, a marking used for both visual and radio identity purposes. However, for the most part this B-17 is referred to by the last three digits of its serial number 42-39988. This number forms the basis of the radio-call number painted on the fin in yellow — 239988 — but it is not the practice to use this form of identification for radio communication in the European Theatre of Operations, the reason being to avoid confusion with other numerical information in radioed messages. Instead, codewords provide an aural identity for aircraft. The most striking marking on the aircraft is the large letter 'C' painted in dark blue on a white rectangle adorning the upper section of the tail fin. Another tactical marking, this distinguishes aircraft of the 96th Bombardment Group of which the 339th is one of four component squadrons. Herring gives the big 'Square C' a glance as he walks round the tail and tries to flex the elevators.

The pilots are back at the entrance door on the right side, their inspection complete. Now they climb into the aircraft to carry out an internal visual inspection of equipment, moving forward to the flightdeck. They start by looking at the tail-wheel assembly and then, squeezing between the two waist gunners, they run their eyes over the control cables stretched along 'the roof' of the fuselage. Next into the radio compartment where the radio operator, TSgt Robert Doherty, is seated at his radio table on the left side sorting out the various codes for the day. Tall and thin, Doherty at 20 is the youngest member of the crew.

Beard sees that the emergency landing gear crank handles are secured on the rear bulkhead of the radio room and that the release handles for the emergency release of the liferaft stowed above the bomb-bay are correctly set. Passing into the bomb-bay the pilots look around to see if anything is amiss, though the armourer and bombardier will have already gone over everything thoroughly. But no one is infallible and there is the odd occasion when even the most fastidious and careful individual misses something. On the flightdeck they find the engineer, TSgt George Goetz, just coming down out of the top turret after installing his guns. 'Reckon you'll need those babies today George. Brunswick is a tough pitch'. Beard grins. 'Yeah, the FWs clobbered the B-24s yesterday. I hear they lost eight', Goetz replies. 'Let's hope our little friends drive them away today', Herring says with feeling.

Apart from a glance to see that the all important fuel transfer valve switch is in the 'off' position, there is no need to check out the engineer's compartment, both pilots know George Goetz is a meticulous engineer and will have double-checked everything. Goetz, who always seems to have a '5 o'clock

shadow' is, at 28, the 'old man' of the crew.

Reaching the cockpit area, Charlie Beard pushes the parachute he has been carrying under his seat. It is a chest pack that can quickly be clipped on to the front of the parachute harness he is wearing. Some pilots wear back-packs which they sit on but it is difficult to move around the aircraft wearing this type.

Pilots' inspection complete, Herring goes into the nose and drops down on to the hardstand through the nose hatch. He signs the Form 1A, accepting the aircraft as mechanically satisfactory and then fills out the crew list, entering all names and the position flown, before handing the form back to the Chief.

The gunners, having installed their guns and attached the ammunition traces, are now outside the aircraft talking. Paul Herring looks at his watch: 'Fourteen minutes then we go'. The crew have 14min to relax before it is time to enter the aircraft and take positions for engine start. Most walk to the nearby hedge and relieve themselves. With the layers of flying clothing this is always a tricky task in the air, so it is better to start with an empty bladder. Bob Doherty attempts to light up a cigarette but the chill northeasterly breeze extinguishes the flame of his lighter. SSgt Everett Johnson, the left waist gunner, puts on his flying helmet for warmth. Johnson, from Connecticut, is a strong, serious young man of 21 and goes by the nickname 'Swede'. He moves into the ground crew shack as do most of the others. Conversation is light, with some levity about experiences with girls in Norwich. No one mentions the mission ahead. Apprehension is hidden but every aircrew member is well aware that it is unlikely to be an easy trip. Brunswick is regarded as being the heart of the enemy fighter land. The target name is not mentioned in front of the ground crew, nor would they enquire, knowing that security is paramount.

Paul Herring and Charles Beard with the Chief are looking up at No 3 engine, discussing the possible reasons for its poor starting record as a Jeep drives up the access track. The brakes squeal as it comes to a halt. An officer beside the driver leans out and shouts to Herring: 'Take-off has been put back 30min.' Without waiting for an acknowledgement the Jeep speeds away to the next dispersal point. Beard curses. 'Shall I tell 'em Paul?' Herring nods. Beard walks over to the shack. Wilson has opened the door, having heard the Jeep and anticipates the delay. 'How long?' he asks. 'Thirty minutes', Beard answers, turning away. There are moans and curses from the shack. Everyone hates these delays and hopes it will not lead to the mission being scrubbed (cancelled). Once keyed up all would rather fly the mission. Someone tries to start up a crap

Above:
A 339th Bomb Squadron ground crew shack at Snetterton Heath. Constructed from salvaged packing case timbers it was primitive but gave shelter from the cold and wet.

game but there is little enthusiasm. The pilots and ground crew continue to review the bomber.

The 30min soon pass. 'Okay fellers, time to go', Beard calls to the men sheltering in the shack. 'Check your harness.' Each man looks at another's harness to see that the webbing is not twisted or bunched tight. In the event of an emergency, loose or twisted harness could cripple a man with the force of his parachute opening and arresting his fall. The bombardier and navigator use

the ground crew's stepladder to enter via the nose hatch. It is possible to pull oneself up into this hatch from the ground, but weighted down in heavy flight clothing this is an exhausting act most can do without. The rest of the crew enter by the rear door except for SSgt Charles Haywood, the tail gunner, who prefers to use the small escape door just behind his station. It is easier than squeezing past the tail wheel stowage and mechanism. The Chief gives his almost ritual 'Good Luck' and then adds 'Give 'em hell for me!'

In the aircraft each man goes to his station. Bill Wood makes sure his bean can is placed near his seat in the nose. It is a joke with the other men, particularly as Woody had the Chief paint the can bright red so there could be no mistaking that it was his. The cold at altitude had a 'go' effect on bladders and while a relief tube is provided in the bomb-bay, this invariably freezes up, negating its purpose. Besides which it is a long way back to the bomb-bay from the nose. Engineer Goetz hangs a pair of GI shoes (ankle cover laced boots) from a coat hanger on the rear bulkhead of his compartment. Like other members of the

Below:
B-17 crew and equipment locations.

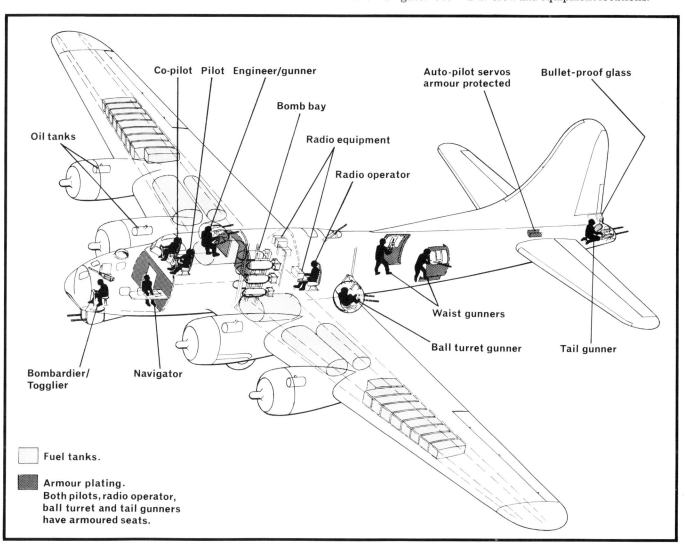

Co-pilot   Pilot   Engineer/gunner

Bomb bay

Auto-pilot servos
armour protected

Bullet-proof glass

Oil tanks

Radio equipment

Radio operator

Bombardier/
Togglier

Navigator

Waist gunners

Ball turret gunner

Tail gunner

☐ Fuel tanks.

▨ Armour plating.
Both pilots, radio operator,
ball turret and tail gunners
have armoured seats.

crew, should he have to bale out the cumbersome fleece-lined flying boots will impede any hope of evading capture; hence the more substantial footwear taken along. Charles Beard has a pair tied to the bottom of his parachute pack.

In the cockpit Paul Herring and Charlie Beard have settled into their seats, the pilot is on the left, the standard position in all US military aircraft with two pilots. The seat waist belt and shoulder straps are fixed, communications lines plugged into jack-points and oxygen hoses to the appropriate regulator valves. Beard takes the check list lodged at the back of the windshield: 'Ready to check?'

'Ready.'

The procedures necessary for correct and safe operation of a B-17 are far too many for a pilot to carry in memory. Men with considerable experience consider they could memorise the actions and sequences, but it was most unwise not to use a check list. Memories are fallible and one vital item missed could cost the loss of the aircraft. Charlie Beard starts to read, moving his left thumbnail down the sheet an entry at a time in order not to lose his place.

'Parking brakes.' This is a co-pilot's duty and he depresses the footbrake pedal, releases the pull knob of the parking brake with his right hand and then re-sets it.

'Parking brakes secure. Hydraulic pressure 750lb; okay.' Beard confirms.

'Release flight control locks.'

Herring reaches down below the central pedestal and releases the lever securing the rudder and elevator locks. He then removes the aileron locking pin which has a red ribbon attached, and stows the pin in the spring clips designed to hold it on the control column.

'Flight controls unlocked.' Herring acknowledges. He then pushes the control column fully forward and turns the wheel right while pushing his right foot hard on the rudder pedals. Beard has slid back his side window and is looking rearward towards the tail. 'Okay, full right rudder, elevators okay, aileron up.'

Herring then pulls the control column right back and turns the wheel left and gives left rudder while looking back out of his side window. 'Flight controls okay.' He flexes them up and down to be sure.

Beard continues with his list. 'Fuel transfer valves off, transfer valves neutral.' He has checked these earlier, now George Goetz, who is standing behind the two pilots, confirms: 'Transfer valves and switch all off.' If they are not turned off, when the electrical power is switched on a pump will start transferring fuel from whichever tank is indicated to another, causing an overflow.

'Fuel shut-off switches open?'

'Fuel shut-off switches open.' Herring acknowledges. These switches, one for each engine, are on the forward part of the central quadrant between the pilots. Their purpose is to give the pilots immediate shut-off of fuel in an emergency, such as an engine fire.

'Cowl flaps open?'

The pilot acknowledges, 'Cowl flaps open and locked left.' Beard then takes a look at the right engines and says 'Cowl flaps open and locked right.' If these flaps on the trailing edges of engine cowlings remain closed when the engines are started there will be a risk of overheating in certain areas of the engine. Also, in the event of an engine fire, fire extinguishers will be more effective as the foam will be drawn through the engine.

'Turbo controls off?' calls the co-pilot. The supercharger is never used during starting as a backfire could cause it serious damage.

'Turbo controls off.' Herring responds.

'Mixture idle — cut off.'

'Mixture controls in engine off.'

'Prop controls full up.'

'Up in high rpm, okay', comes the acknowledgement.

'Throttle closed and set.' Herring pulls the two throttle levers back and then edges them forward slightly to give the appropriate 1,000rpm which will make engine starting easier. As with the previous four checks, these controls are located on the central console.

'Auto pilot off.' Herring checks switches at the back of the quadrant.

'Okay, auto off.' While the auto pilot can be overpowered by the normal controls, it is easy for a pilot to be preoccupied during take-off and if left on, the auto pilot could precipitate an accident.

'Carburettor filters on.' Beard glances at the small panel on his right which has a switch and an amber 'on' light to indicate each filter is open. He then calls 'Intercoolers'. These controls are also located on the co-pilot's side of the cockpit and he checks the four sliding levers are in the bottom of their quadrant on the 'cold' mark. This ensures that once the turbo-superchargers are running the compressed air they produce will be cooled before reaching the carburettors. In flight, when severe freezing conditions are encountered, the intercooling setters can be moved towards 'hot' to prevent carburettor icing.

The proper anti-icing equipment features in the next check call from the co-pilot: 'Prop anti-icer switches.' Paul Herring puts his hand down on two dial-type switches on a box projection at his left. These control tiny jets of de-icing fluid which are sprayed along the leading edges of the propellers to prevent ice forming thereon. Adjacent is a switch to activate vacuum operated de-icers on the leading edges of the wings and tailplane, but in the 8th Air Force these pulsating black rubber bladders, known as 'boots', have been removed. It was found that if dislodged and torn through battle damage the de-icer boots could hazard aircraft safety by jamming aircraft control surfaces. 'Yeah, prop de-icers are off okay.'

'Cabin heat off' is the next call. Herring checks the lever on his left marked 'Cabin Air'. It is already at 'Off' where he left it at the end of the last flight. This is a hot air system generated by utilising the circulated exhaust from No 2 engine to heat glycol through a radiator. The 'off' position allows cold air to pass through the glycol radiator to prevent boiling.

'Generators off.' The electrical generators are kept off until the engines are started.

'Generators off,' Herring calls as he looks at the pilot's side panel on the left of the main instrument panel.

'Uncage flight indicator and gyro.' Herring checks the levers at the base of these two gyroscopically controlled instruments in the top centre of the main instrument panel. They are normally never touched unless the aircraft is being taxied over very rough ground. These instruments provide indications of direction and flight attitude with reference to the horizon. 'Gyros okay', Herring acknowledges.

Then, finally, 'Landing gear switch.' This should be in the central position with a guard in place to prevent accidental movement. But it is essential to check it is not in the 'up' position for once the electrical system is made live the landing gear would retract. The switch is on the co-pilot's side of the central quadrant. Beard reassures himself with an emphatic 'Landing gear switch is down.'

The cockpit check complete, Paul Herring looks at his hack watch; there are two-and-a-half minutes to engine start. The term hack watch is derived from the practice of the Intelligence Officer calling 'hack' for all airmen to synchronise wrist watches at the end of the briefing session. The pilot looks down through the left side of the windshield to see if the Chief is in position. The Chief is there, standing out in front of Nos 1 and 2 engines, holding a fire extinguisher and in just the right position where he can see the pilot. Herring turns to Charlie Beard: 'Is the assistant crew chief in position?' Charlie nods.

Herring looks at his watch again: 'One minute and 52 seconds.' They sit, now aware of the chill breeze coming in the cockpit side windows. Paul Herring secures his flying helmet under his chin. There is an unusual silence; no aircraft noise on the base or in the sky. Only the wind in the nearby trees can be heard at this time. Seconds tick by with the weight of hours at this juncture. It is a time when the reality of this situation invades men's minds. Who won't be coming back today? Mentally, Herring recites the 23rd Psalm as he has always

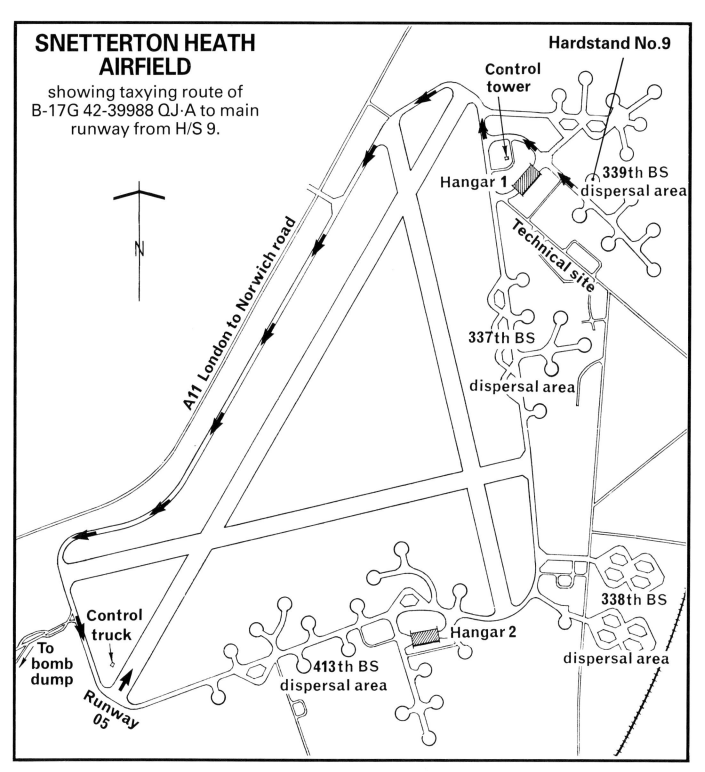

SNETTERTON HEATH AIRFIELD

showing taxying route of B-17G 42-39988 QJ·A to main runway from H/S 9.

Hardstand No.9

Control tower

Hangar 1

339th BS dispersal area

Technical site

337th BS

dispersal area

338th BS

dispersal area

Hangar 2

413th BS dispersal area

A11 London to Norwich road

N

Control truck

To bomb dump

Runway 05

Above:
Snetterton Heath Airfield.

done before a combat mission. He checks his watch again, impatiently. Seventeen seconds to go, then suddenly somewhere else on the field an engine splutters into life: somebody has jumped the clock. He grins at Charlie Beard, 'An eager beaver, huh!' Then, putting his head out of the side window, he yells 'Clear Chief?' Beard calls 'Clear!' out of his window and slides it shut.

With his left hand the pilot flips the three battery switches on his panel, then with his right, the master 'bar' ignition switch on the main console is pushed on.

He does not have to check the battery condition or inverter operation, knowing the Chief has previously given these a thorough test. There are three 24V batteries, one in the left wing leading edge near the root and two in a similar location in the right wing. The two inverters, located one under the pilot's and the other under the co-pilot's seats, convert the 24V direct current of the electrical system into the higher voltage alternating current necessary to operate some panel instruments and the radio compass. One inverter is a spare. Next Herring turns on the fuel booster pump switches, just to the right of the main bar switch. These electrical pumps

provide fuel at around 8lb pressure to the carburettors for engine starting. An independent back-up fuel supply system, the booster pumps also prevent vapour lock in fuel lines at high altitude.

Now Herring puts up a finger and makes a circular movement with his hand to the Chief, indicating he is about to start No 1. The Chief raises a hand in acknowledgement. 'Start 1' Herring orders. Beard presses down the start switch for No 1 on his engine starter panel at the extreme right of the main instrument panel. Immediately there is a whirring from the left outer engine as the starter builds up its flywheel speed. After about 15sec, while still holding the starter switch down, he shifts the same hand to hold down the switch alongside marked 'Mesh'. This pushes the starter clutch into the engine and immediately the prop starts to turn. With his right hand Beard gives strong steady strokes with the hand primer, which feeds atomised gasolene into the top five cylinders of No 1 engine. After only half a revolution the propeller jerks, the engine flies into life and the propeller blades disappear into a barely visible arc. Beard releases the starter switches and the hand primer while Herring removes the mixture control on the central console to the position marked 'Auto Rich'. This allows automatic metering of fuel at the carburettor's rich jet in response to throttle settings.

Herring watches the left hand engine oil pressure gauge as the pointer for No 1 engine rises (there are pointers for both Nos 1 and 2 engines on this instrument). It takes about 15sec to reach the desired 70lb/sq in and meanwhile Herring adjusts the throttle slightly so that the engine rpm is registering around 1,000. So far so good. Now No 2 engine. Herring closes his side window to lessen the song from No 1, and turns to Beard and shouts

Below:
B-17 Instrument Panel
 1. Fluorescent light switches
 2. Pilot's oxygen flow indicator, warning light and pressure gauge
 3. Co-pilot's oxygen flow indicator, warning light and pressure gauge
 4. Voltmeter (AC)
 5. Radio compass
 6. Emergency oil pressure gauge (Not on G)
 7. Flux gate compass
 8. Hydraulic oil pressure gauge
 9. Suction gauge
 10. Altimeter correction card
 11. Airspeed alternate source switch
 12. Vacuum warning light
 13. Main system hydraulic oil warning light
 14. Emergency system hydraulic oil warning light (Not on G)
 15. Bomb door position light (Not on G)
 16. Bomb release light
 17. Pilot's directional indicator
 18. Pilot's localiser indicator
 19. Altimeter
 20. Propeller feathering switches
 21. Airspeed indicator

 22. Directional gyro
 23. Rate-of-climb indicator
 24. Flight indicator
 25. Turn-and-bank indicator
 26. Manifold pressure gauges
 27. Tachometers
 28. Marker beacon light
 29. Globe test button
 30. Bomber call light
 31. Landing gear warning light
 32. Tailwheel lock light
 33. Flap position indicator
 34. Cylinder-head temperature gauges
 35. Fuel pressure gauges
 36. Oil pressure gauges
 37. Oil temperature gauges
 38. Carburettor oil temperature gauges
 39. Free air temperature gauge
 40. Fuel quantity gauge
 41. Carburettor air filter switch
 42. Oil dilution switches
 43. Starting switches
 44. Parking brake control
 45. Spare fuse box
 46. Engine fire extinguisher controls (on some airplanes)

'Start No 2!' and 'Mesh No 2!' No 2 engine starts equally as well as No 1. Now the same procedure is carried out on No 3 engine which has a history of reluctance to start from cold. This time it starts with no more complaint than a hefty blast of flame from the exhaust. Herring watches the oil pressure intently but it comes up well within the critical 30sec. Finally, No 4 engine; this also starts easily and runs smoothly.

Right:
Controls at Co-pilot's right
 1. Hydraulic hand pump
 2. Checklist
 3. Interphone selector switch
 4. Interphone jackbox
 5. Filter selector switch
 6. Co-pilot's seat
 7. Rudder pedal adjustment
 8. Co-pilot's control wheel
 9. Intercooler controls
 10. Suit heater outlet
 11. Engine primer

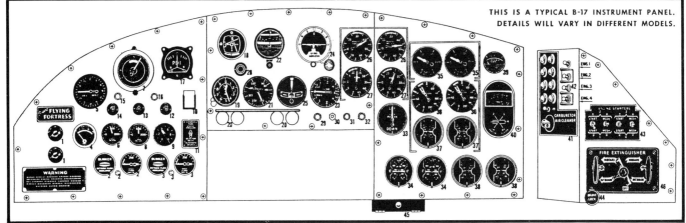

THIS IS A TYPICAL B-17 INSTRUMENT PANEL. DETAILS WILL VARY IN DIFFERENT MODELS.

Left:
Controls at Pilot's Left
1. Panel light
2. Panel light switch
3. Pilot's seat
4. Filter selector switch
5. Propeller anti-icer switch
6. Interphone jackbox
7. Oxygen regulator
8. Windshield wiper controls
9. Portable oxygen unit recharger
10. Windshield anti-icer switch
11. Windshield anti-icer flow control
12. Propeller anti-icer rheostats
13. Surface de-icer control
14. Aileron trim tab control
15. Pilot's seat adjustment lever
16. Aileron trim tab indicator
17. Cabin air control
18. Suit heater outlet
19. Vacuum selector valve
20. Emergency bomb release

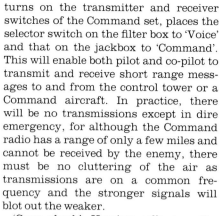

The next task is to verify that the vacuum pump is providing the correct amount of suction for the gauges. This is to ensure that the flight indicator, an instrument that depends on vacuum, will operate correctly. Herring sees that the required four inches of pressure is registering on the gauge before he turns a selector on the fuselage side to his left to bring the other vacuum pump into operation, and this shows a similarly satisfactory output. This, while Charlie Beard runs through another 11-point check list on instrument monitoring to check that readings are satisfactory. Herring now turns his attention to the radio controls situated in the ceiling panel of the cockpit. Reaching up, he

Above:
Control Panel and Pedestal
1. Ignition switches
2. Fuel boost pump switches
3. Fuel shut-off valve switches
4. Cowl flap control valves
5. Landing gear switch
6. Wing flap switch
7. Turbo-supercharger controls (B-17F)
8. Turbo and mixture control lock
9. Throttle control lock
10. Propeller control lock
11. Propeller controls
12. Throttle controls
13. Mixture controls
14. Recognition light switches
15. Landing light switches

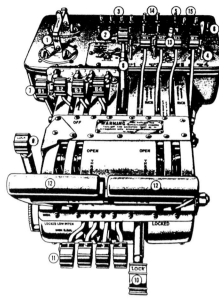

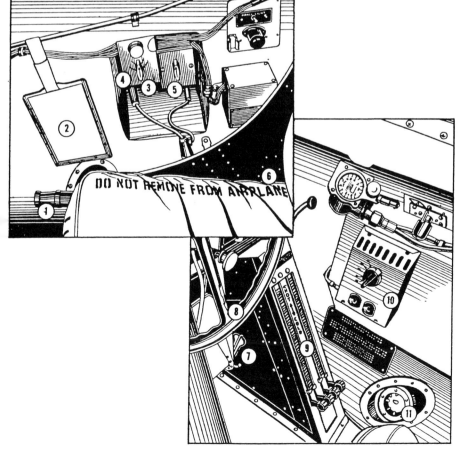

turns on the transmitter and receiver switches of the Command set, places the selector switch on the filter box to 'Voice' and that on the jackbox to 'Command'. This will enable both pilot and co-pilot to transmit and receive short range messages to and from the control tower or a Command aircraft. In practice, there will be no transmissions except in dire emergency, for although the Command radio has a range of only a few miles and cannot be received by the enemy, there must be no cluttering of the air as transmissions are on a common frequency and the stronger signals will blot out the weaker.

'Crew check', Herring calls over the interphone. Every member of the crew has a throat microphone and earphones with leads plugged into the jackpoints at their station. Herring then calls each position by position name: 'Tail gunner' and Charles Haywood replies 'Tail gunner', and so on until all crew members have acknowledged. This confirms to the pilot that all are in position and that their interphones are working correctly.

While the co-pilot and engineer continue to monitor the instruments, the pilot notes that the altimeter reading is correctly set at 150ft, the height of Snetterton Heath above sea level. An incorrect setting could be hazardous if the weather closed in on return from the flight, with the risk of flying into high ground. Fortunately, Snetterton Heath is located in Norfolk, one of the flattest counties in England with no real high ground within 100 miles.

Herring makes a sweep away gesture with his left hand to the Chief. This is in order to remove wheel chocks. Beard makes a similar sign to Apperson on his side of the aircraft. Both ground crew men take a circuitous route to the landing gear, approaching from the rear, for spinning, near invisible, propellers have claimed the lives of several careless mechanics. When the chocks have been pulled to the side of the hardstand the Chief returns to a point ahead of the aircraft where he can be seen to signal that the task has been accomplished.

It is now 0855 and the control tower has given a coded radio message to the leader of the formation in which *The Iron Ass* will fly, to commence taxying. Paul Herring consults his mission flimsy, a sheet of rice paper on which times, codewords and other vital information for the day's operation are given. Rice paper is used so that it can be easily destroyed — eaten if necessary. The 96th Bomb Group was the first in the 8th Air Force to become a double group, that is, a doubling of its complement giving it the capability of flying two different group formations, designated 'A' and 'B' on a single mission. Today it is putting up an 'A' Group, to be lead group of the whole Division force going to Brunswick, while the 'B' group, to which *The*

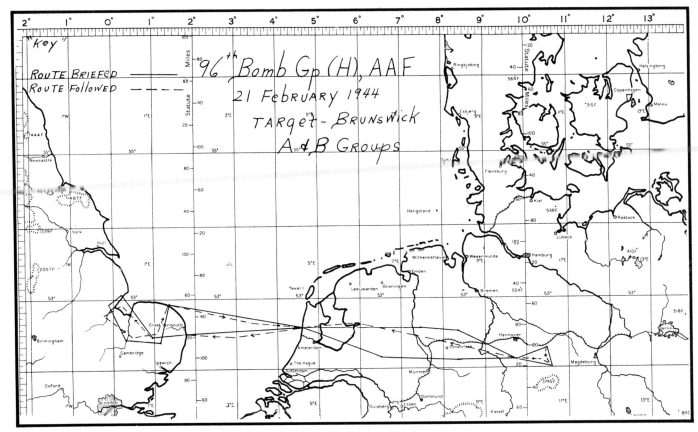

Above:
**Route plan of mission to Brunswick –
21 February 1944.**

Iron Ass is assigned, will fly 2,000ft lower than the 'A' Group and about half-a-mile behind.

The first squadron of 'B' group is taxying out. The whole airfield reverberates to the whine and throb of engines — 152 Wright Cyclones totalling 182,000hp. At some 30 other bomber stations across the East Anglian plain a similar volume of noise arises and resounds over the surrounding countryside. The launching of the whole mission is audible over an area approaching 5,000sq miles as more than 800 B-17s and B-24s with 8,000 crewmen prepare to take over 4,000 tons of high explosive to the enemy. The force will use two million gallons of fuel and will be carrying some five million rounds of ammunition.

'Bookie: roll' — the radio message is short and to the point. 'Bookie' is the call sign of the 339th Bomb Squadron. Beard depresses the brake pedals and releases the parking brake. The ground crew have positioned the bomber so that it faces straight down the access track so there is no need to release the tail wheel pivot lock. Herring retards the throttles on the inboard engines to 700rpm and advances those of the two outer engines to push up rpm to 1,200. The design of the throttle levers allows smooth manipulation of any combination. *The Iron Ass* begins to roll forward down the access strip, accelerating to a fast walking pace. Charles Haywood, the tail gunner, knows the moment the aircraft

begins to move by the immediate lessening of the fuselage tremor at his position. Haywood is an Oklahoman, a self-reliant 24-year-old, gentle but tough. He and Bill Wood are the only two married men on the crew.

A B-17 is passing the end of the access to *The Iron Ass*'s dispersal point: 'That's Wunnenberg in QJ:M. We want QJ:S don't we?' Beard queries. 'Yep, 657 S-Sugar, Seaman's ship', Herring answers. 'Number three in line. We're four.' They are referring to the identification letters on the other B-17s taxying by. It is important that they join the traffic pattern on the perimeter track in the correct order. With the slightest touch on the brakes Herring brings *The Iron Ass* to a halt about 30yd from the intersection. An old B-17F model (no chin turret) is waiting its turn to move on the opposite side of the taxiway. 'L-Love. That'll roll after we go', Beard says. He has his left earphone pulled higher up his head and Herring, likewise, has his right earphone away from his ear. This enables the two men to converse without going through intercom, but they have to raise their voices in order to be heard above the engine noise.

'Okay, here comes S-Sugar. Unlock the tail wheel', Herring orders. Beard reaches down to the right and moves the locking lever towards the floor. 'Tail wheel unlocked', he responds.

While waiting to turn on to the taxiway Herring retarded the throttles on the two outboard engines, now he again advances them but briefly runs the right one up to 1,300 revolutions which had the effect of turning the Fortress left

on to the taxiway about 70yd behind the bomber ahead. From now on Herring will use the outboard engines to manoeuvre the bomber. He cannot see ahead over the nose so he uses the edge of the taxiway on his side as a guide. Beard watches the right side; the taxiway is only 50ft wide and a main wheel over the edge could mean becoming stuck in the soft earth. With a 15mph northeast wind prevailing, the main runway has been scheduled for take-off entailing a haul of nearly two miles to reach the far end of the airfield from the 339th dispersal area. After rounding the northern curve of the perimeter track it then runs straight for three-quarters of a mile, parallel with the A11 London to Norwich road. On this stretch Beard re-locks the tail-wheel pivot as it makes it easier to control the bomber on a straight run.

Halfway down this stretch Goetz, who is still standing behind the pilots, warns that the B-17s ahead are stopping. Brake shriek can be heard above the whine of the engines. Herring slowly brings *The Iron Ass* to a halt, knowing the strain involved in bringing a moving 30 tons to rest. Imprudent or careless use of brakes in such circumstances can quickly burn out linings. As soon as the brakes are on, Herring revs up each engine in turn to 1,500rpm to clear the spark plugs. On the rich mixture being used the sooting of plugs can happen quickly at low engine speeds. Herring knows that the aircraft ahead have come to a halt for the same reason. Presently the 'cab rank' of B-17s is on the move again. Chuck Haywood in the tail gun position keeps his eyes on the Fortress behind, ready to

18

Above:
Take-off and landing record – 21 February 1944.

(Take-off and landing form — handwritten table)

TAKE-OFF AND LANDING
(To be filled in, in order of take-off)
Date: 21 February 1944

Station ___
Mission ___ GROUP

Squadron	Position	Airplane Serial No.	Pilot	A/C Letter	Take-off	Landing	
338	Lead -2	10-053	Litowitz	M	0905	16:18	7:40
8	-3	10-920	Watts	N	0906	16:19	7:40
8	-4	10-924	Solan	K	0907	16:17	7:40
8	-5	10-174	Stone	Y	0908	16:20	7:40
8	-6	10-810	Long	B	0909	16:18	7:36
8	-1	10-021	Sterler		0910	16:28	
		Ship form 42nd					
339	High -2	10-094	Donovan	M	0915	16:23	7:40
9	-3	10-894	Munnenberg	K	0911	16:24	7:40
9	-4	10-091	Seeman	S	0915	16:21	7:40
9	-5	10-988	Herring		0913	13:17	4:30
9	-6	P10-470 A	Byron	G	0911	1357	4:10
9	-6	P10-570 A	Simons				
		Ship from 42nd					
431	Low -2	11-567	Knox	K	0916	16:26	7:40
3	-3	11-970	Hanrick	E	0917	16:24	7:40
3	-4	11-403	Sims	L	0918	16:27	7:40
3	-5	11-924 A	Dennisen	P	0919	13:08	4:30
331	-6	11-520	Brandau		0920	16:05	
33	-6	U 814	Saw	S	0956		
5-4	-1		Ship from 42nd				

M43

140 Dropped
10 Jettisoned
10 Unknown
20 Returned

Right and Below right:
Mission briefing forms – 21 February 1944.

warn his pilot if it gets too close. While taxying the pilots try and maintain about 30yd separation between each bomber. It takes 14min to complete the journey to the head of runway 05, the northeast-southwest aligned runway, which is a mile-and-a-quarter long. The six B-17s of the lead squadron of 'B' group are already on the runway undergoing pre-take off checks. The second squadron, in which *The Iron Ass* is to fly, comes to a halt and the pilots also commence the pre-take off ritual. If an engine is not functioning properly it is as well to find out now. A faltering engine on take-off can bring a critical situation. The B-17s, as is usual, have an overload of bombs and fuel and the loss of an engine on take-off will most likely precipitate a crash.

The Iron Ass, built by the Lockheed Vega factory in California, has electronic turbo-supercharger controls. For Herring and other pilots this is one of the most notable improvements to the B-17. Previously the turbos had hydraulically actuated controls which were prone to freezing or sluggish operation at high altitudes, a constant worry for pilots. With brakes applied, Herring calls 'Take-off check — tabs', while checking the aileron, elevator and rudder trim tab controls to see all are set at the zero mark and not extended. 'Tabs — set zero', he calls and then: 'Wing flaps

(Mission briefing form 1 — handwritten)

Target: Dr
Force against Target: 45CW followed by 13th CW, 4min later
4th CW will follow 13th CW, 4min later. Course on 0870E. by 4 min to attack target on
Friendly Activity: 3 division forces to depart Cromer as Zero plus 12 min on airfields East of Ruhr.
2nd division forces to depart Cromer at Zero plus 28 and will attack targets East of Ruhr.

Take Off: B 0835 A 0855   Runway Direction SW to NE   Surface Wind NE 15

Group Assembly: Place Southern Kirtle
Time B 0940 A 0950   Altitude B 17000 A 9000
Assembly Route: Base - 15500 - 1031 ; 96B from S.W. ; 452 from E.
1047 ; Boston - 19500 - 1051 ; 5308-0014E - 18700
; Ely - 22020
Climb 150 M.P.H. I.A.S. and 300 to 10000 ; Spl #5 - 17000 ; Spl #6 -
Zero Hour 1130   Altitude
Route Out: Splasher #6 (22000) to Splasher #5 to 5236-0439E to
5234-0728E to 5231-0820E to 5207-0944E (IP) to Target

I.P. 5207-0944E   Time 1326
IP to Target: Mag heading 73   Distance 30   Turn Left
Bombing Altitude - A 22000   B
Bomb Load: - A 10 x 500 % x 100   B
Turn from Target: Right   B Same
Secondary Target: None
Last Resort: See Reverse side
Route Out: Rally (5200-1035E) to 5207-0944E to 5207-0819E to 5210-0630E to 5236-0439E (Start Descent) to Lowestoft to Bases.

(Mission briefing form 2 — handwritten)

E.T.A. English Coast 1519
Target Altimeter Setting 0956
Last Possible Time of Take-off

Miscellaneous: Last resort — Any airdrome in enemy occupied territory not adjacent to a populated area or any industrial target positively identified in Germany that can be attacked without disrupting fighter support.

Gas Load 2700

The B wing of each C.W. formation will begin to take interval for bombing at 5231-0820E. C.W. formation will resume after bombing.

Pathfinder bombing of lead ships drop on flares and smoke bombs.

For take-off 96B Climb on 319° to 6000 then left. 96A Climb on 307 to 5000 then Rt.

Flares 96A R&YY   Aldis 96A Amber
452 YG   B Red
45A Violet

19

up'. The co-pilot sees that the flap control switch is in the fully 'Up' position.

Advancing the throttles to 1,500rpm, Herring tests the propeller pitch change. He runs the propellers from the 'High' rpm setting to 'Low' rpm and back again, which changes the blade pitch, while he watches the 300 to 400 drop in rpm on the instrument panel tachometers. Satisfied that the pitch change functions properly, he calls 'Prop pitch okay' and then 'Generators on', flipping the four switches situated in the middle of the pilot's control panel. The aircraft is now generating its own electrical power and the ammeters surge in response.

'Starting engine run-ups: No 1.' Herring opens up No 1 engine until the manifold pressure gauge registers 28in and briefly switches out one of the two magnetos and then the other. Beard watches to see there is no more than a drop of 50 to 75rpm when running on one magneto, while Herring studies the cowling and nacelle on No 1 engine. If there is any roughness in the ignition it will be more evident through a slight twisting movement of the engine nacelle than through the rpm shown on the instruments. As ignitions appear satisfactory, both magnetoes are switched in and No 1 run-up momentarily full throttle to observe the manifold pressure — 36in is registered. This input pressure into the engine cylinders varies slightly, depending on the atmospheric conditions prevailing. The higher the pressure the better the prospect of power delivery. In the USAAF manifold pressure was expressed in inches of mercury whereas the RAF used pounds/sq in and termed it 'boost'. The other three engines are now run up in the same way to check their ignitions.

The next action is to see that the turbo-superchargers are operating correctly. Throttle lever for No 1 engine is moved until 1,500rpm shows on the tachometer. The turbo boost selector on the right of the central console is turned to give 46in of manifold pressure and the throttle lever is then fully advanced to see if the correct manifold pressure and rpm readings are obtained on the instruments. This is found to be in order, so power is reduced before the same procedure is carried out to exercise the other superchargers.

As Herring and Beard finish their concentration on the run-up procedures, they see that four B-17s of the first squadron have already taken off and that the fifth has just begun its roll.

Beard: 'Hey, the ship ahead's Wunnenberg's QJ-M. What happened to Seaman?'

Goetz: 'I'll take a look from the turret.' Goetz goes back to the top turret where he can obtain a good all-round view.

Herring: 'Well, he went by us back there.'

Goetz comes on interphone: 'Skipper, he's the other side of the runway head.

He came round the east side of the perimeter track.'

The B-17 ahead of *The Iron Ass* has started to move on to the runway. Beard releases the parking brake and the tail-wheel lock. 'Parking brake off. Tail-wheel lock off.'

Herring advances the throttle slightly and moves *The Iron Ass* to the head of the runway. As soon as the B-17 they have been following starts its take-off, Herring turns his aircraft on to the 150ft-wide runway, coming to a stop when he has positioned it centrally.

'Lock tail-wheel', he calls to Beard and receives the reply: 'Tail wheel locked. Warning light out.' After a brief pause Beard calls, 'Gyros!' Herring reaches forward to adjust the directional gyro on the instrument panel to correspond with the magnetic compass above the windshield. It reads 05, which is the known bearing of the runway about to be used. 'Gyros set.'

'Generators.' Beard is reading from his pre-take off check list.

Herring: 'Generators on.'

'Fuel booster pumps.'

'Booster pumps are on.'

'Auto Rich?'

'Manifold pressure set Auto Rich.'

'Props?'

'Props high rpm.'

'Clear to go.' Beard's final call almost meets the double flash of green light from the black and white checkered runway control van parked to the left of the runway head. A B-17 nosepiece fixed to the roof of the van serves as an observation dome. The controller watches each Fortress lift from the far end of the runway and then gives a signal with his Aldis lamp for the next aircraft to follow. The interval between each take-off is about a minute.

In the rear of *The Iron Ass*, the two waist gunners have positioned themselves in a sitting position with backs to the radio room and bulkhead. Ball turret gunner Dearmon has fastened the safety strap on the auxiliary seat in the radio room where he sits for take-off. These are precautions against injury if there were to be a crash on take-off. On some B-17 crews the bombardier and the navigator prefer to ride on the flight-deck until the aircraft is safely airborne for the same reason, but Wilson and Wood remain in the nose. Flight Engineer Goetz stands behind the pilots as he has to monitor the instruments as a back-up to the co-pilot. Herring takes the pressure off the foot brake, selects 46in of manifold pressure and opens the throttles. He does so with the palm of his right hand in an upward stance with the fingers hooked over the horizontal bars of the levers. This permits an easy wrist movement, advancing the throttle smoothly and progressively leading the left and right engines as required to keep straight down the centre of the runway.

The Iron Ass picks up speed steadily. Past the first runway intersection a third of the runway has gone and the airspeed instrument shows 60mph. Herring can feel the rudder biting as he applies light movement on the pedals with his foot to maintain the central position on the runway. This is also an indication of sufficient speed for the elevators to be effective and a little back pressure on the control column lifts the tail sufficiently for the tail-wheel to leave the ground. He holds this tail-low position, maintaining a good angle of incidence for the wing that will cause the aircraft to fly itself off the runway once sufficient airspeed has been reached. Charlie Beard has taken over the throttles, holding them with his left hand to make adjustments while he watches the manifold pressure, rpm, fuel and temperature gauges and has the other hand ready to work the emergency switches if a turbo or propeller overspeeds. All Herring's attention is focused outside the plane. With the tail-low sit of the bomber he still cannot see directly ahead over the nose and watches the runway edge for guidance. The intersection of the third runway flashes by as the speed mounts to 100mph and Herring eases back on the column, but there is no response. Normally he should be airborne at this point. Herring has a stab of apprehension: 'Come on you son of a bitch', he murmurs in exasperation, just as the vibration signifying adherance to the concrete ceases. The Fortress has lifted off.

Moderate back pressure is maintained on the control column as the runway threshold disappears below the nose. A thumbs up sign from the pilot indicates to the co-pilot to raise the landing gear. They have been through this so many times, actions are near automatic, without need for signs. Beard gently applies the brakes to stop the main wheels revolving and then moves a switch to bring the landing gear up. This is achieved by electric motors powering screwed rods. A quick glance out of the pilot's window confirms: 'Left gear up', while Beard gives 'Right gear stowed', before replacing the operating switch in the neutral position. Usually the waist gunners report on the tail-wheel and as no report is heard Beard calls: 'Wake up you guys. Tail wheels?' Over the interphone, response comes quickly; 'Sorry sir, sure it's up.'

With the heavy load aft there is a tendency for the B-17 to climb steeply so pressure on the control column is reduced. The climb is kept at a shallow angle to let the speed build up. Looking out of the nose, Bill Wood, watching the trees, hedgerows and farmsteads that

dot the Norfolk landscape diminish in size, feels relief. Apart from the busy pilots, take-off is an anxious time for the rest of the crew. They know what happens to a B-17 full of bombs and fuel that falters when separating from the ground.

At a mile out the IAS (Indicated Air Speed) is the required 150mph and Herring brings the throttles back until the manifold pressure reading is 38in. Beard is ready to follow with a reduction in rpm from 2,500 to 2,300 by adjusting the pitch controls. The rate of climb is now approximately 300ft/min.

Some two miles out from the base Herring eases the control wheel right and begins a gentle turn to the south-east. A course of 319° has to be flown to 6,000ft to take the bombers through the overcast. The B-17 that took off before *The Iron Ass* can be seen about two miles ahead, also turning, and beyond that the aircraft of the lead squadron. *The Iron Ass* is to be lead of a three-plane element in the high squadron of the 'B' group. Herring continues the turn until the flight indicator moves to 319. He levels out and now holds this course, applying a little aileron trim to overcome a slight left wing down tendency. There is a broken overcast above at about 2,000ft which, for safety, decrees that the

Centre right:
The leadship of 96th 'B' Group, flown by Capt Litowitz on the mission described. Officially B-17G 42-31053, BX:W of 338th Bomb Squadron, it was nicknamed *Stingy* **at the request of Maj-Gen Fred Anderson, when head of VIII Bomber Command, for his small son.**

Right:
Winnie C, **B-17F 42-6099, leadship of the high squadron.**

21

Left:
Two 96th Bomb Group B-17Gs gain height above the clouds.

formation assembly be made above the clouds.

'Pilot to tail gunner. How many do we have behind, Haywood?'

'Three to take off, the rest are behind us.' From his perch in the tail, together with the climbing attitude of the aircraft, Chuck Haywood has a good view of the Snetterton Heath.

'Roger, tail gunner,' comes the acknowledgement from the cockpit.

At 2,000ft Herring tells Beard to switch off the fuel booster pumps. It is SOP (Standing Operational Procedure) to keep these working until a reasonable height has been gained, purely for safety in case an engine-driven pump fails. Charlie Beard checks that fuel pressures are satisfactory and then returns his attention to cylinder head temperature gauges, closing the cowling flaps slightly. These flaps, ringing the rear of the engine cowlings, produce considerable drag and it has been found that in some conditions cylinder head temperatures will be higher with the flaps fully open than with them partly closed. The gauges show a little over 200° centigrade.

At 2,500ft *The Iron Ass* starts to pass through the base of the overcast. 'Pilot to bombardier and navigator. Keep a good look out. I've lost sight of the ship ahead.'

'Roger, Skipper.' Most pilots, being captains of aircraft, are dubbed Skipper.

Suddenly the bomber is completely enveloped in the grey mist. 'Bye bye England', Swede Johnson exclaims, as his view of the English countryside from the left waist window suddenly disappears. Goetz, still standing behind the pilots, strains his eyes into the greyness ahead. The risk of collision is very real in the congested sky over East Anglia. Today, however, with the 96th Bomb Group leading the Division to Brunswick, the Snetterton Heath B-17s are the first into the sky, which lessens the probability of a collision.

The cloud layer is extensive and it is several minutes before an increase in height brings a breakout. At 4,670ft *The Iron Ass* bursts into a bright world with a dazzling sun low in the east throwing the clouds into bold relief: darkened rifts and snowy crests. The cold bleak

Centre right:
In this view from the radio room top hatch, a gentle turn allows following bombers to cut the corner and gain their positions as wingmen.

Right:
The world of dazzling sunlight, white cloud tops and dark shadows was an exhilarating sight after leaving the grey mists of a 'solid' undercast. The lead squadron has formed its vee flights of three B-17s.

February day below has been transformed.

Herring continues to hold the required 319° course to the stipulated 6,000ft. At this altitude a right-hand turn is begun. Now he reaches up to the radio compass controls in the cabin roof and switches them on. In the United Kingdom the radio compass has been adapted to work with the short range radio beacons situated at selected locations for the specific purpose of enabling the American heavy bombers to assemble formations over an undercast. Known as Bunchers, once every minute these ground stations transmit a Morse call-sign, which is received on the small rotatable loop aerial under the nose of the Fortress. Control boxes on the navigator's table and in the pilot's cabin roof provide a means of tuning, while an instrument for the navigator and another on the cockpit panel display a bearing to the signal source. Herring

turns the control wheel a little more and then brings the aircraft out of the turn on course to Buncher No 9, situated at Snetterton Heath. In the nose John Wilson is also watching the radio compass dial and checking on the signal aurally. He makes a note in his log of the position and time. Other B-17s can be seen ahead as the climb continues. A red flare burns in the distance. Bill Wood comes on interphone: 'Bombardier to pilot. Red flare at one o'clock. Our lead squadron?'

'Roger, bombardier. I see it. Yes, single red is "B" Group, yellow is "A".' Herring refers to the flares periodically fired from the lead aircraft of a formation to identify it for those who must assemble behind. Each group is assigned a different colour or colour combination in red, yellow or green.

As the altimeter shows nearly 10,000ft, Beard nudges Herring and points to this instrument. Herring nods and reaches out, turning off the carburettor air filters. He then turns on the fuel booster pumps, calling, 'Carburettor air filters off, fuel boosters on'. The carburettor filters are not left in place after this altitude as the reduction in atmospheric pressure tends to cause a rise in carburettor temperatures, which has a detrimental effect on fuel mixtures. Also due to the decreasing atmospheric pressure as altitude increases, there is a tendency for the suction of the engine-driven fuel pumps to cause vapour lock in the lines. The booster pumps increase the pressure in the supply lines and prevent vapour lock.

Next Beard calls on the intercom: 'Co-pilot to crew. Oxygen; repeat, on oxygen.' Those men who had their oxygen masks hanging loosely under their chins now button them into position and see that the hose connections are firmly in the oxygen regulators at their stations. Each then turns on the flow at the regulator. The proper mixture of air and oxygen is now supplied automatically, the percentage of oxygen increasing as does the altitude at which the aircraft is flying. This device makes use of decreasing atmospheric pressure to effect the correct mixture, which is only supplied when the wearer of the mask inhales.

It is SOP for the crew to go on oxygen at 10,000ft. Although normal breathing does not appear to have been affected, the diminishing amount of oxygen causes slight lethargy and discomfort for some individuals. Bob Doherty fully opens the warm air outlet shutter in his compartment. The outside temperature is also diminishing with altitude. Bob can see little strips of ice on the frame of the open gun hatch above him. While all crew members on the B-17, other than the waist gunners, have the benefit of ducted warm air, this is only really effective for those in the forward part of the aircraft. Both waist gunners and Chuck Haywood in the tail have been using their electrically heated flying suits since soon after take-off.

Heavy sheepskins are worn to obtain extra protection against the icy blast coming through the waist windows and they also serve as a back-up to the heated suits which are notorious for failing. For Chuck, who sits with his legs bent and resting on knee supports, there is the regular problem of hot spots occurring where the electric suit is doubled up. Some of the new Douglas-built B-17Gs recently received by the 96th Bomb Group, have enclosed waist positions, which are staggered, one slightly forward of the other, affording much more room for each gunner to work without getting in the way of the other as well as keeping out the icy blast. *The Iron Ass*, a Vega-built aircraft, still has the open-type waist positions.

At the call for oxygen, Roger Dearmon has left the comparative comfort of the radio room and gone back to enter his ball turret. Like most men who fly the ball turret, he has left entry as long as possible. The gunner's position is cramped and he will have to spend the next five hours curled up with his legs spread apart. The name 'ball' is not official, but has become the general term due to the shape of this turret suspended under the fuselage of the bomber. Dearmon uses a hand crank to bring the entry door uppermost, in which position the guns are pointing vertically down. The door also serves as back protection, being partly made of armour plate. He steps in and positions himself on the seat and then closes and locks the door behind him. As soon as oxygen and interphone connections are plugged in and the safety belt attached, Dearmon pulls on the hand grips to elevate himself and the turret to the horizontal plane. Today, on entry, there were only clouds to be seen, but on many occasions the gunner is confronted with a vertical view of the ground, perhaps two miles below. It is no place for the squeamish or men with a tendency towards claustrophobia. The ball gunner's station is remote and lonely. There is no room for his parachute and in an emergency he has to position the turret so the door can be opened before climbing back into the fuselage to put on his 'chute'. Ball gunners know that they may not have time to do that. They have seen other B-17s disintegrate in a matter of seconds; it can take a minute to vacate a ball turret.

Paul Herring has been watching the needle on the radio compass dial. Suddenly it completely reverses position, indicating that he has passed directly over the transmitting station. He starts a left-hand turn and, having reached 11,000ft, the briefed height for making group assembly, will fly an approximate 10-mile orbit, using the Buncher signal as a marker point.

'Co-pilot to crew; oxygen check.' Beard has given the crew a few minutes to set up their oxygen supplies and to check their individual pressure gauges and flow indicators. He then continues calling each member of the crew except the pilot, by crew name position, starting with the tail gunner and working forwards. Each man acknowledges by repeating his crew position. On this occasion everything is satisfactory. A serious oxygen problem can lead to abandonment of the mission, an abort, and no one wants to abort, even for genuine reasons. There are turnbacks by some aircraft on nearly every mission, and while the vast majority are for genuine reasons, no one wants to be the subject of doubt.

Herring makes an adjustment to the turbo controls. The rate of climb is now reduced to approximately 200ft/min. The B-17s are arcing left, another red flare appears, falls and dies.

'Right waist to pilot. Ship QJ:L is now off to the right.'

'Roger, right waist. Tail gunner, what have we got back there?'

Haywood surveys the scene from his tail turret. Two B-17s are to his right some way off and a third is coming up on the right about a quarter-of-a-mile away. 'Tail to pilot. Our wingman is about 500yd back and down, off the left wing.

Below:
A view from the high squadron of the low squadron's lowest and rearmost flight in 'Purple Heart Corner'. The three-plane flight or element was the basic building block of formations.

Two other '17s are about half-a-mile out to your left.'

'Thanks tail gunner.' Herring turns and looks back over his shoulder and then comments to Beard: 'That'll be our squadron lead who took off late.'

The Iron Ass is flying towards the sun again and both pilots pull down tinted goggles over their eyes. White cloud tops stretch to the horizon; all is bright in contrast to the grey scene left at Snetterton. Ahead another red flare. The six aircraft of the lead squadron are gradually coming together in two flights. Below, 96 'A' group is also forming. It has been briefed to assemble 2,000ft below 'B' group.

Another crossing of Buncher 9 is made completing another orbit; altitude is now 13,000ft. *The Iron Ass* has been airborne just over an hour. By shortening its turns the B-17 off the left wing, QJ:G, is now in position with QJ:A, *The Iron Ass*, its nose about level with Chuck Haywood's position in the tail but echeloned down and to the side about 150ft. The other B-17 of the element, QJ:L, has now positioned on the right of *The Iron Ass* but higher and echeloned back. The lead flight of the high squadron is also now loosely formed.

Beard again calls each position for an oxygen check, he or someone designated by Herring will do this every 15min throughout the flight. An oxygen failure is not easily noticed if an individual is distracted and he may quickly become unconscious. A regular check is an essential lifeline. B-17 crewmen have died through anoxia on several missions, so no chances are taken.

Below:
Perspective block diagram of 3rd Bomb Division formation.

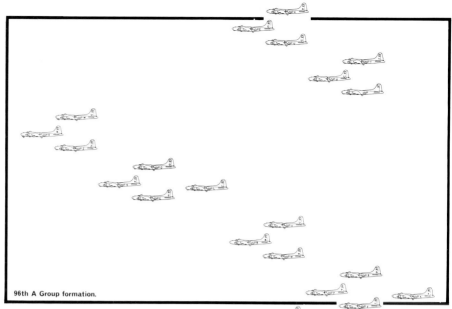

96th A Group formation.

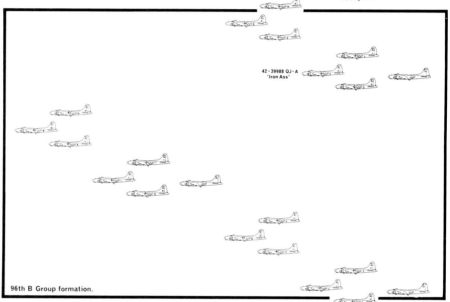

42-39988 QJ-A
'Iron Ass'

96th B Group formation.

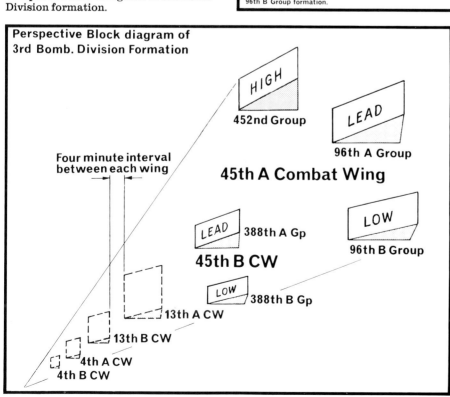

Perspective Block diagram of 3rd Bomb. Division Formation

HIGH
452nd Group

LEAD
96th A Group

Four minute interval between each wing

45th A Combat Wing

LEAD
388th A Gp

LOW
96th B Group

45th B CW

LOW
388th B Gp

13th A CW

13th B CW

4th A CW

4th B CW

Top:
Formation – 'A' Group.

Above:
Formation – 'B' Group.

At 1035hrs another orbit has brought *The Iron Ass* towards the Snetterton Heath buncher again, altitude 15,500ft. All six aircraft of the high squadron are now in position, as are those of the lead and low squadrons. An additional B-17 of the 452nd Bomb Group from another base was scheduled to position at the back of each squadron to bring the 'B' group formation total to 21 aircraft, but these B-17s are nowhere to be seen. The 96th 'B' group formation is otherwise complete and only a minute late for the scheduled rendezvous with 96 'A' group in the vicinity of Buncher 9 on a course northwest to point 5303N-0014E on the Lincolnshire coast. As the 'B' group formation approaches from the southwest, Bill Wood sees they are converging with another formation. He goes on interphone: 'Bombardier to pilot. Looks like we're on the ball. Our "A" group ahead — they're firing yellow yellows —

Above:
'A' Group in the lead and 'B' Group echeloned back below. This two-wedge formation was designed to give gunners fields of fire as free as possible from obstruction by other bombers.

and we will come in about two miles behind and 500ft higher I guess.'

'Thanks Bill. Let's hope our lead ship has seen them.' The recognised acknowledgement on interphone conversation is 'Roger'. Sometimes individuals lapse into more casual exchanges. These men have been together on 12 successful combat missions and work smoothly as a team.

At 1111hrs the 96th 'A' group, about two miles ahead, is turning left and the leader of the 'B' group begins to turn in order to position to the left rear of the 'A' group when the turn is completed. These turns are deliberately planned to enable the various formations to locate in the desired positions, building squadrons into groups, groups into combat wings and finally combat wings into the Division column. The next dog leg course is to Boston town, a good landmark in the Lincolnshire farmland, and then southeast to Ely, another prominent landmark. The cloud has become more broken and the lead navigators can pinpoint landmarks seen to confirm the position, although cur-

rently it is a combination of DR (Dead Reckoning) and radio aid navigation.

While the lead navigators of the 96 'A' formation are now deciding the course for all following aircraft, individual navigators will still plot their own course in case of a need to separate from the formation due to personnel or equipment failure. Already John Wilson sees that the formation has left the brief heading and has turned too soon. The task force commander in the lead formation is obviously trying to make up some of the time lost when the take off time was put back half-an-hour. Wilson estimates they will now be several miles south of Boston but the cloud is thickening and will probably prevent ground checks. Although the 'B' group took off first and assembled at a higher altitude, it has been briefed to fly as a low group to the 'A' group. At the time 'A' group turns southeast for the leg to Ely it is at 19,000ft and the 'B' group at 18,500ft. With this turn the 'B' group leader brings his formation into the desired position, echeloned back on 'A' group with a separation of 1,000ft, achieving this by a slight reduction in his angle of climb. It is now a case of follow-the-leader and a good formation leader considers the problems of the pilots who will be following. All turns have to be gradual otherwise those on the outside of the turn will fall behind or

have to increase power an undesirable amount to stay with the formation while, alternatively, those on the inside of the formation will have to cut their speeds and run the risk of stalling. Any abrupt change in flight attitude or speed by the leader can threaten the flight security of a following formation.

'Ball turret to pilot; contrails.'

'Roger, ball turret.'

The hot gases from the engine exhaust, mixing with the frigid air, creates condensation trails in areas of high humidity. They stream out behind each engine, merging with the contrails of other bombers to form cloud-like bands stretching back for miles. From his vantage point below the belly of *The Iron Ass*, Dearmon can see all the other B-17s in 'B' group. At this time the slightly higher 'A' group is not throwing contrails, one of the peculiarities of this phenomenon is that contrails appear and disappear at different altitudes.

'Left waist to pilot. The wing ship has peeled off.' This is followed immediately by 'Top turret to pilot. QJ:G looks like he's aborting.'

'Roger.' Herring turns to Beard; 'That's Simons. Wonder what the problem is?' A B-17, aborted through some problem, has turned back towards base.

Charlie Beard is concerned that the cylinder-head temperatures have risen

Above:
The first traces of contrails appear as the formation gains altitude. The aircraft in the foreground, 42-39814, BX:S, was shot down on the mission described.

past 205°C in the two outer engines, the optimum figure for the safe operation. He eases the cowl flaps open a little to effect more cooling, but knowing that this will also bring additional drag.

Herring nudges Beard: 'Okay Charlie, you take her.' Beard takes the controls. There is no laid down policy on when a co-pilot flies but, like most pilots, Herring will alternate with Beard about every half hour until they reach the target.

'Tail gunner to pilot. We have another B-17 formation at 5 o'clock high.'

'Thanks; that'll be the 452nd. Watch them.'

The 452nd Bomb Group are scheduled to provide the high group of the combat wing of the three groups, which is the van of the 3rd Division force. This Division is leading the 8th Air Force attacks this day and will be followed by the 1st Division (B-17s) and the 2nd Division (B-24s). A high pressure area

Right:
Contrails mark the passage of the formations and make their location easy for enemy defences.

over Germany is giving clear skies and the 8th Air Force is taking advantage of this in a campaign against the German air force and aircraft industry.

At 1113hrs the 96th 'A' group lead starts to make his brief turn over Ely for the leg on which combat wings assemble in prescribed order. John Wilson continues to make his own plot and estimates the mission leader is still trying to make up time by shortening the dog legs. This leg should be towards

the medium range beacon at Scole, designated Splasher 6, but the lead formation, 96th 'A' group, is heading northeast of Splasher 6, shortening the assembly course. The final turn to the left should enable all combat wings to position correctly in the divisional column. The point of departure from the English coast is at Splasher 5, a radio beacon situated near the coastal town of Cromer. The departure time at this point is known as Zero Hour, on which the

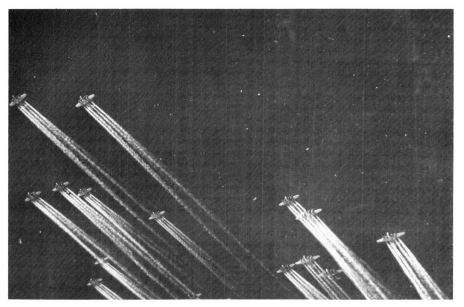

time planning for the whole mission has been worked out.

The leader of 96th 'B' group has levelled off, climbing to 20,300ft and then dropping the nose to pick up speed and levelling off at 20,000ft. The purpose of this manoeuvre is to let the B-17s build up full momentum for level cruising. Going directly from climb attitude to level flight tends to cause the aircraft to mush with a heavy load and this can be dangerous in close formation. The briefed level-off altitude is 21,000ft but the lead group is flying at this height so the 'B' group has no option but to position at 1,000ft below. Beard reduces the manifold pressure setting to 34in and then synchronises the propellers back to 2,200rpm. The cylinder-head temperatures slowly drop back from 210°C. The oil temperature also declines. The climb completed, the strain on the engines is reduced.

Beard motions to Herring: 'Looks as if the lead box is not going to go any higher.'

'Yeah, perhaps they'll raise it over the sea.'

The box is a term for a group formation because, in designing the positions of the aircraft within a formation to achieve the best defensive layout, the formation is conceived to occupy a cube of airspace. Visually, the three group formations that form the 60-plane combat wing, take the form of an angled wedge.

'Okay, I'll take it.' Herring takes control and Beard gives another oxygen check call to the crew.

'Left waist to Pilot; there are two boxes of B-24s heading at us at 10 o'clock level.'

'Roger, left waist, I see them.' Herring judges they are not on a collision course and will pass below and behind.

'At 1200hrs precisely *The Iron Ass* passes over Splasher 5 as the formation starts to turn on to the cross sea course. They're half-an-hour behind the planned time for departing the English coast, a delay that may cost them fighter escort at some point ahead. It has taken two and three-quarter hours to form the bomber formations and gain the required altitude necessary for penetrating hostile airspace.

The gunners are now charging their guns — feeding the ammunition trace into the breech blocks. For most gunners assembly time is one of boredom. Even the breathtaking spectacle of the contrailing bomber formations begins to pall after a while. For those in the rear of the aircraft attention is focused on keeping warm. Outside temperatures are now 50° below freezing, minus 20°C. Non-operational talking over the interphone is discouraged so there is little to do but think and check your oxygen regulator. 'Ike' Iacoviello sings to himself but with his throat mike switch off no one can hear his renderings of popular ballads.

John Wilson leaves his navigator's table to charge the two nose side guns and returns to keep his log. He continually re-checks his calculations. His bomber may be following a formation but a good navigator never loses track of his position. Today might be the occasion when knowing exactly where they are will be the deciding factor as to whether they can return home safely. *The Iron Ass* has a Gee box installed, a device which allows very accurate position checks to be made through the transmissions of Gee ground stations in the UK. Occasionally Wilson checks his calculations against the Gee readings. He has no need to keep the pilot informed as they are locked into following the formation leader. Even if the mission leader veers far from the briefed route you follow and hold formation.

At some 25 miles out from England, Wood springs his chin turret trigger arm over from the right side of the nose into its operating position. He goes on intercom: 'Okay, test-fire your guns. Watch where you're firing.'

Brief bursts of gunfire sound above the persistent roar of the engines. A whisp of smoke passes through the flightdeck from the nose. Herring hands over the controls to Beard again and goes on interphone: 'Pilot to Engineer; pull the Tokyos.'

'Roger, Sir', comes the reply. This order concerns opening the valves on the Tokyo tanks allowing fuel to drain by gravity into the main tanks. George Goetz inhales deeply, uncouples his oxygen line and drops down from his turret. He opens the door to the bombbay, steps down on to the catwalk and proceeds to the rear bulkhead where he pulls tee-shaped handles on either side of the rear door before hurrying back to the flightdeck. His next action is to quickly reconnect his oxygen supply. As it takes an average 30sec to carry out this fuel switching duty, Goetz does not use a portable oxygen supply. The task Bill Wood now sets out to perform requires more time, and he unplugs his oxygen connection and fits it into a yellow and green painted walk-around bottle located near his position. He then stoops down and goes back up to the flightdeck, making a thumbs-up sign to Herring as he opens the flightdeck to bomb-bay door and steps down on to the narrow catwalk. He then proceeds to remove the arming pins from the fuses of the 10 bombs. This will allow the arming vanes — which are like miniature propellers — to turn when the bomb falls and fully arm the bomb.

Beard notices that they are starting to slip back on the lead flight of the high squadron. He glances at the airspeed indicator. It registers 150mph (true airspeed 207mph) so he increases the rpm a little, opens the throttle and turns in another 2in of manifold pressure. The airspeed indicator needle moves steadily up to 160 IAS. The airspeed indicator

instrument is worked through atmospheric pressure and as this declines with increasing altitude so the indicated airspeed becomes further removed from the true airspeed.

'Right waist to pilot. We have lost our right wingman. He's turned back.'

'Roger, right waist.' 'That's Lynch's ship.' Herring says to Beard.

With the second abort *The Iron Ass* flies alone in the high squadron spot in 'B' group. 'Better bring her over to fill in the diamond slot', Herring orders. Beard eases the control wheel right to take the bomber away from the formation and then immediately reverses his turn. This action places *The Iron Ass* further away from the lead flight and allows Beard to bring the bomber into a position directly behind the high squadron leader, making it a four-plane flight.

'Left waist to pilot. We lost another. A ship's just dropped out of the low squadron with a feathered prop.'

'Roger, left waist.'

The strain on engines hauling 30 tons through the sub-stratosphere is severe and turn-backs through engine failure are a feature of most missions. The position has improved considerably since the introduction of electronic turbo controls. The B-17Fs and very early G models have hydraulically actuated controls which need constant attention as the oil tends to thicken in the cold temperatures. If not frequently exercised, oil is lost and turbo overspeeding and failure may follow. Electronic turbo controls have made the pilots' workload considerably lighter.

At 1231hrs John Wilson comes on interphone; 'Navigator to pilot. Landfall enemy coast.'

'Roger.' There is only cloud below. Wilson's plot tells him that they have reached 5236N-0439E, a point on the Dutch coast north of Ijmuiden. Wood comes on interphone: 'Flak suits.' He is referring to the body armour made of overlapping thin steel plates inside canvas aprons. They are heavy and cumbersome and most crewmen do not like to wear them any longer than necessary. However, flak suits have saved many lives and the discomfort is endured. There is no compulsory rule about wearing flak suits in this crew; some men prefer to wait until the flak starts bursting. As yet the sky is clear of the familiar black puffs. The formation alters course, southwest.

The German radar and listening posts had alerted the defences that a major mission was being launched from England over an hour ago. Now the enemy defence controllers speculate on the objective of the American bombers. Sometimes convoluted routes are planned expressly to keep the enemy guessing as long as possible. The top and under turrets of *The Iron Ass* are constantly on the move as Goetz and Dearmon scan the sky for any sign of enemy fighters. It would be unusual to

Above:
The bombers forge ahead through enemy airspace. The higher formations are at the prevailing contrail level while the B-17s 1,000ft lower are clear. Higher still a formation of protecting P-47 fighters crosses the bomber stream.

receive an attack so early in the mission, the Luftwaffe usually waits until the escort fighter's range is fully stretched. Dearmon turns the hand grips in his turret, slowly swinging the turret through 180° in azimuth. He tries to avoid pointing the guns forward too often as the icy slipstream enters round the gun barrels.

'Top turret to pilot. Little Friends above.'

'Roger.' Herring looks up. 'Little Friends' are escort fighters. Five or six thousand feet above the bomber formation the familiar weaving contrails of four P-47s are visible. Another four can be seen high to the north. A reassuring sight.

Bob Doherty checks his watch. On the hour and half-hour he listens on the Division frequency for recall or any other coded Morse messages. His gun waves idly above in the open hatch. He glances up for a sight of the escort but from where he sits there is nothing to be seen but deep blue.

A half-hour on, at 5234N-0728E, the lead group changes course on to an easterly heading. Herring takes over the

controls again. Beard notices a rim of ice adhering to the outer framing of the cockpit side windows so he increases the cabin heating.

'Tail turret to pilot. Flak at 4 o'clock.' There is an element of excitement in Haywood's voice.

'Roger, tail gunner.'

Luigi Iacoviello strains his head over his gun. He sees a few of the dreaded black smoke puffs far away.

'Navigator to crew. We're over Germany, fellers.' There is no response. Eyes just scan the sky more intently. Beard calls for an oxygen check. It is 1330hrs, approximately half-an-hour's

Below:
'Flak so thick you could get out and walk on it' was the famous quip.

flying time to the Initial Point, the selected point over which the bomber force will turn to make its run on the target.

The undercast shows no sign of breaking; it appears that the attack will have to be on radar sightings. With that possibility in view, the two leading aircraft of the 96th 'A' group are PFF (Pathfinder Force) B-17Gs of the 482nd Bomb Group fitted with H2X ground scanning radar sets of which, at this date, only 10 are operational within 8th Air Force. The 100nd Bomb Group, based at Alconbury, specialises in radar bombing. These two participating PFF B-17s had flown to Snetterton prior to today's mission to take off with the 96th

'A' group. If the weather clears and visual sighting can be carried out, a number of depot airfields are to be bombed, but it appears that the weather forecasters have been too optimistic with their prognosis.

Below:
A flight of P-51 Mustangs some 5,000ft above the Fortresses; a comforting sight. The higher cruising speed of the fighters necessitated weaving back and forth in order to stay with the bombers.

Bottom:
Nearing the Initial Point, 96th Bomb Group Fortresses become hidden in thickening contrails.

At 5231N-0820E the formations make a slight change in direction. The escort weaving high above the bomber column are now P-51 Mustangs, the longest ranged of the three types of US fighter on today's operation. At this last directional change the combat wing that has been flying off to the left of the lead combat wing starts to come in trail in preparation for the bombing run. There is approximately four minutes' flying time between each combat wing.

'Ike' Iacoviello has noticed that a retaining screw in the breech of his .50 gun is loose. The vibration of the airframe causes it to turn slowly. He takes a screwdriver from a canvas bag attached to the mount, but it is difficult to hold in the heavy electrically heated gloves he is wearing. He removes the glove to reveal an inner silk glove. The screw is tightened quickly, for the silk glove gives only minimal protection and frostbite is an imminent risk. Ike quickly replaces the electric glove. He has seen what frostbite can do to the unprotected hands of gunners; not a pretty sight.

At 1358hrs the IP is reached and the lead group fires yellow-yellow flares to warn of the turn. As the formation goes into the turn, flak blossoms between 96 'A' and 96 'B' groups. The range, if not the aim, is accurate. 'Holy cow!' somebody in *The Iron Ass* exclaims. Black smudges hang in front of the high squadron, then suddenly they are among the Fortresses and gone. Everyone waits for the next salvo. It does not come. The low squadron of 'B' group finds it is running through patches of light cloud and for once radio silence is broken. The group commander comes over the Command radio: 'Chairback Red; climb one thousand angels.' He repeats the call. Herring has the controls and advances the turbos a little. Beard increases the propeller setting to give more rpm as Herring opens the throttles in preparation for the climb of 'B' group.

Suddenly the interphone is filled with shouts: 'Bandits, 12 o'clock low!' 'Focke Wulf, 11 o'clock low!' Bursts of machine gun fire drown out the voices. *The Iron Ass* shudders. Then the roar of engines takes over again. 'What happened?' The pilots saw nothing of this action. Smoke wisps pass them and the scent of burnt cordite finds its way through into oxygen masks.

'An FW came through us. I picked him up at 800yd with the chin turret and gave him about 20 rounds,' Wood relates excitedly. Dearmon cuts in: 'He went under our left wing. I gave him a burst. He was smoking.'

'I saw him go, he was hit, he was smoking,' Iacoviello adds. In the excitement of the moment correct interphone procedure is forgotten. A *Staffel* of Luftwaffe fighters had made a climbing attack at 'B' Group, passed through and dived away. The action had lasted but a

Above:
Waiting in the waist. A gunner maintains his watch for enemy interceptors. The open position exposed gunners to extremely low temperatures and oxygen masks had occasionally to be squeezed to dislodge ice formations on the exterior.

few seconds. This was the usual nature of these clashes.

'He's a probable . . .' Dearmon starts to say, but suddenly changes the subject; 'Ball turret to pilot. A B-17 in the low squadron has a wing on fire.'

'Roger, ball turret.'

'Yeah, there's fire . . .' Johnson remembers he is not using the correct interphone procedure and starts again. 'Left waist to pilot. Low squadron B-17 with left wing on fire and diving away.'

'Roger, left waist, Who is it?'

'Left waist to pilot. Think it's a 338th ship, "S" for Sugar, flying the Purple Heart Corner.' Purple Heart Corner is the lowest, rearmost and most exposed flight in a heavy bomber formation and for this reason is often selected for

attack by enemy fighters. Little wonder B-17 crews joke that to fly there puts one in a good position to be awarded the Purple Heart (the medal given to all wounded).

Dearmon has the best view and watches as the burning Fortress slides away from the formation. flames streaking back from main fuel tanks. He averts his gaze to swing his turret in search but when he brings it back again the stricken Fortress is nowhere to be seen.

'Fighters! 3 o'clock level.' FW190s pass through the formation. There is a crack and the pilots of *The Iron Ass* feel vibration on the controls; it becomes severe on the rudder pedals. The bomber slides out of formation. Beard reaches down and pushes in the automatic pilot switch. The gyroscopic-based electrical instrument has the ability to compensate for unnatural flight forces far more smoothly than a human. Beard also brings back the throttles and this minimises the vibration. *The Iron Ass* is losing height, as Herring has to put the nose down to prevent a stall.

'Tail turret to pilot. We've been hit. Pieces are flying off the fin.'

'Pilot to tail. Have you been hit?'

'I see no blood; I think I'm okay.'

'Looks like the tail is breaking up. Do you want us to bale out?' someone says.

'No, we've got control', Herring responds. He and Beard adjust the power controls: turbos, throttles, propellers. They have lost nearly 1,000ft and Herring elects to join the low squadron, gradually pulling up to the rear of the lowest flight. Increasing the power increases the control vibrations. Beard shakes his head. Herring catches his eye; 'If I can hold her until bombs away I think we can make it.'

'Top turret to pilot. Looks like we took a 20mm in the fin and the slipstream is peeling off bits of skin. I can't see any other hits.'

'Roger, thanks top turret.'

Bob Doherty remembers he is scheduled to start pushing out bundles of chaff four minutes before the target. Chaff is the name for the thin metallic foil strips which, when released in large

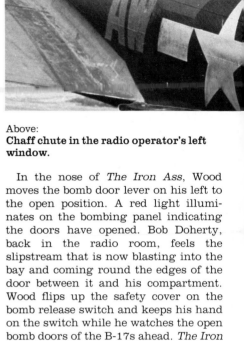

Above:
Chaff chute in the radio operator's left window.

In the nose of *The Iron Ass*, Wood moves the bomb door lever on his left to the open position. A red light illuminates on the bombing panel indicating the doors have opened. Bob Doherty, back in the radio room, feels the slipstream that is now blasting into the bay and coming round the edges of the door between it and his compartment. Wood flips up the safety cover on the bomb release switch and keeps his hand on the switch while he watches the open bomb doors of the B-17s ahead. *The Iron Ass* has no bombsight installed, like all the other B-17s except the lead and deputy lead of each squadron. Normally the bombardier in the leading bomber sights for the whole formation, other bombardiers releasing on the leader's signal. But today it seems unlikely that anyone in the leading formations will be able to use a bombsight for visual attack and all aircraft will have to drop on the release of the two PFF B-17s. At 1406hrs the bombs of 96 'A' group go down. Two red flares are fired by the leader as well as illuminating the signal lights at the back of the tail gun position. A few seconds later 96 'B' group leader unloads

Below:
Radio operator's view above: another B-17G is framed against the contrails left by the fighter escort.

Above:
2Lt Wood's combat report.

quantities, saturate the screens of the enemy's gun-laying radar. There is a small chute on the left hand side of the radio room and Doherty picks up the bundles, rips off their binding and pushes them through the aperture. It is good to have something physical to do as for most of the mission he sits, listens and thinks. Today it also helps to break up the trauma of watching the vertical stabiliser do a strip-tease.

The run from the IP to the target is some 20 miles and the 96 'A' group is about to make its drop. The two PFF B-17s have their nose radomes extended; there are no satisfactory breaks in the clouds so the drop will have to be 'blind' — by radar.

32

Above:
***Tarfu* makes its drop. The change in engine note told the crewmen that their B-17 had parted with its load.**

on the white plumes from the smoke markers dropped by the PFF aircraft. Immediately Woody sees bombs descending from the bay of the Fortress directly ahead he hits the release switch. There is a distinct change in engine note and *The Iron Ass* literally lifts a few feet as it is rid of two-and-a-half tons of steel and high explosive.

A total of 130 × 500lb bombs descend from the 13 B-17s remaining in 96 'B' group and if all releases were prompt they will explode within an area roughly 250yd wide by 500yd long. The devastation wrought goes unseen by the deliverers, who now turn right towards the brief rally point, 5200N-1035E. The turn allows the groups to re-form their relative defensive positions within combat wings.

Woody moves the bomb door lever to the closed position and then goes on interphone: 'Bob, will you check the racks.'

'Roger, bombardier.' Doherty reaches forward and unlatches the door. He is

Right:
Ten 500lb GP bombs drop in train from *Ruth L III* (leading), *Kipling's Error III* (nearest camera) and other 96th Bomb Group B-17s. The interval setting should theoretically give a line of strikes 30ft apart.

relieved to see that all bombs have gone, even though it will not be his job to dislodge any that may have hung up, which occasionally happens. Then it requires someone with a wrench or bar to force the bomb's lugs off the offending shackle. An undesirable task as it has to be performed with bomb doors open and no parachute clipped on. Doherty goes on interphone and reports to Wood that the bomb-bay is empty.

Bereft of bomb loads the formation speed has again increased to 160 IAS (224mph true airspeed). By locking the rudder Herring and Beard have stopped the oscillation that produced the severe

vibration. They have also been able to increase power sufficiently to keep up with the low squadron. It is an undesirable situation and the hope is that *The Iron Ass*'s predicament does not draw the attention of an enemy fighter.

West of Osnabrück flak blossoms, each brief burst of flame thrusting steel splinters upwards. Fortunately both range and aim is inaccurate; the black smoke smudges pass half-a-mile away to the right.

Wood is using his little red can and Dearmon a screwtop hot water bottle for the same purpose. Beard passes Herring coffee from a Thermos flask and Herring

Above:
A different intervelometer setting places these 500-pounders to strike in pairs. Leading aircraft is *Messy Bessy*.

Left:
The view vertically down from the bomb bay as a mixed bomb load descends towards the clouds.

Above right:
Bomb doors closed, MZ:A of the 413th Bomb Squadron, 96th Bomb Group heads for home.

Right:
The Combat Wing reforms its defensive position for the flight home.

pushes his oxygen mask to one side so that he can drink. John Wilson works intently on his course charts. If the pilots cannot keep up with the formation they may have to come home alone and then it is essential to know exactly where you are. Iacoviello reports more flak on the right side, but bursting much higher than the formation.

'Tail gunner to pilot; just seen another piece of the stabiliser come away.'

'Roger, tail gunner. We'll get her home.' Herring's voice is confident.

At 1530hrs John Wilson reports they are over the Zuider Zee. Bob Doherty turns on his Liaison set in case there are special instructions from Command if the weather has closed in over England. Happily, it now seems to be improving and there are glimpses of water and land

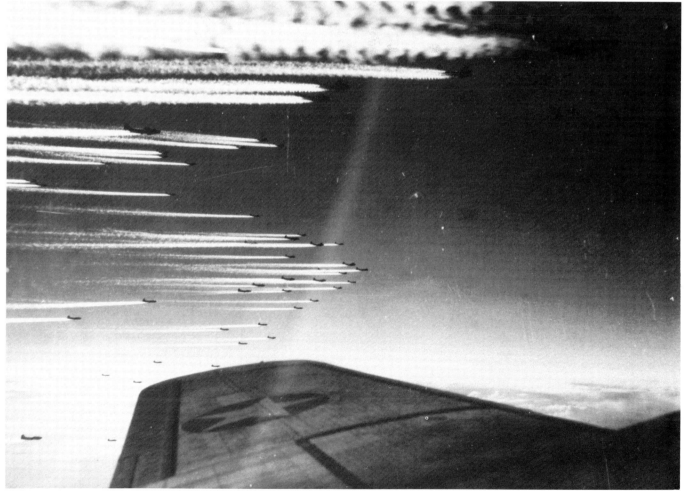

Above:
More P-47s arrive to cover the withdrawal in another view from the radio room gun hatch.

below. Goetz still revolves his turret. Despite the 50-below temperature outside, the sun through perspex warms the back of his head. It is difficult to search the sky with the same concentration. Like most of the gunners, he has learned to regularly shift his gaze to the aircraft around him; continually looking at the blue void above soon has you seeing spots.

At 1525hrs at 18,500ft comes the news that all have been anticipating. 'Enemy coast', John Wilson announces. Everyone has a sense of relief. The gunners still have to be on guard but the Focke Wulfs and Messerschmitts are unlikely to trouble them now. Bob Doherty looks up out of the radio hatch and sees the familiar twin booms of two

Below:
The sun breaks through the gloom as the group lets down over the sea. It may look pretty, but in a winter ditching the water temperature is so low life expectancy is brief.

P-38 Lightnings far above. It gives him a brief sense of elation.

'Left waist to engineer. I've got some trouble with my oxygen regulator. Can you take a look now?'

'Pilot. Okay to go?' Goetz asks. He gets permission, slides down out of his turret and clips on an oxygen bottle. Still stiff with sitting, he is pleased to make the track back through the bomb-bay to the waist positions. There is a leak at the left waist oxygen supply point; some part of the regulator seems to have been damaged. Goetz tells Johnson to use a walk-around bottle as the formation is now letting down rapidly. Goetz returns to his position and checks the fuel gauges. There is still ample fuel and fairly evenly distributed so there is no need to transfer fuel between tanks.

At 1540hrs Beard sees the altimeter is showing 10,100ft. 'Okay, crew you can go off oxygen.'

'Glory be!' someone exclaims. 'I'm for a pee-pee', another voice echoes on the interphone. There is relief all round. Bob Doherty removes his mask and starts to eat a chocolate bar he had in his pocket. The earphones weigh heavy on his ears but he cannot stop his listening watch until the bomber is safely on the ground again. Herring calls for carburettor air filters on and fuel booster pumps off. The formation begins to spread out. It makes it easier for pilots and there is not the risk of getting into the turbulence of an aircraft ahead. There is, however, still need for vigilance as they descend into cloud. Collisions can easily occur in these circumstances when men are tired and less cautioned. There will be some unwary pilot who doesn't hold his course.

The cloud becomes more broken as the Fortresses fly west. Then comes the first glimpse of surf and land; the English coast. It is 1559hrs. A coastal town, Lowestoft, comes into view. Landfall is right on the briefed point. The gunners start removing the ammunition trace from their guns and making them safe. Accidents are all the more likely to happen when men are tired.

Dearmon swings his turret so that the hatch at his back is uppermost. He goes on intercom, 'Ball turret to waist gunners. One of you guys like to give me a hand out.'

'Okay', comes the reply. Iacoviello goes to the turret and holds open the hatch while Dearmon slowly extracts himself. 'The darned electric suits has burnt in around the knees again', he shouts into Iacoviello's ear. Iacoviello grins: 'Yeah, I could smell you cooking!' After hours cooped up inside the ball it takes Dearmon a bit of stretching to ease himself. Chuck Haywood has come out of the tail. He too is suffering from sitting in one position after such a long period.

The formation continues to lose altitude. The cloud is now reasonably broken and the English countryside here and there bathed in afternoon sunshine. The formation flies over three airfields where B-24s are landing and within 15min of crossing the coast Snetterton Heath comes into sight.

Herring reaches up and switches on the Command radio to transmit. 'Bookie A-Able to Chairback; Bookie A-Able to Chairback. We have battle damage. Request instructions for landing. Over.' Chairback is the Snetterton control tower callsign. The response is prompt. 'Chairback to Bookie A-Able. Do you have good control or do you want priority?'

'Bookie A-Able to Chairback. We have tail damage. Rudder vibration.'

'Okay Bookie A-Able, we'll have you in after the lead squadron. Over and out.'

'B' Group has been airborne longest and is scheduled to land first. While it does, 'A' Group makes a wide orbit of the airfield at 2,000ft. 'B' Group flies past the north side of the airfield at some two miles away and just under 1,000ft from the ground. The flights now separate, breaking left with the aircraft curving round and falling into trail to approach runway 05.

'Okay, check list.' Herring has removed his helmet and is telling Beard directly. Beard takes a card and calls the checks out: 'Ball turret.' Goetz, who is standing behind the pilots, leans forward and says, 'Ball turret checked'.

Below:
The first squadron starts to peel off to land; those elements on the right side go first.

This means that Dearmon has extracted himself and that the hatch has been closed and the turret elevated so that the guns are on a horizontal plane again. If kept pointing down they would strike the runway on landing.

'Crew positions.'

Bob Doherty comes on interphone: 'Crew in position'. The ball gunner and the tail gunner are in the radio room and the waist gunners backed up against the rear of the radio room bulkhead.

'Auto pilot.' Herring leans over: 'We'll wait until we're on final.' He is overriding the auto pilot with the manual controls but wishes to retain the stabilis-

Above:
The homecoming: ground crew men appreciate seeing a good formation and even after a long hard mission the fliers like to oblige.

ing effect of the auto pilot as long as possible.

'Booster pumps on.' 'Mixture Auto Rich.' 'Intercoolers off.' 'Carburettor filters on.' 'All okay.' Beard completes his checks.

The Iron Ass is curving round over the small town of Thetford. Herring only has to drop the left wing a little to achieve this, such is the inherent stability of the Fortress. He keeps the

airspeed registering just under 180mph as, due to the tail damage, he intends to make a faster than normal landing. He calls: 'Landing gear down'. Beard moves a switch. Each pilot takes a look out of his respective side window as the wheels unfold, slowly revolving in the slip-stream.

'Left gear down.' 'Right gear down.' The green indicator light shown on the control panel as Beard returns the switch to the neutral position. Herring checks the hydraulic pressure gauge to see there is sufficient pressure for the landing brakes. A Fortress will need far more than a mile-and-a-quarter to stop if the brakes don't function.

Goetz comes back to the pilots: 'Tail-wheel down okay'. He has been back to give a visual check and re-check the ball turret position. Herring levels *The Iron Ass* out at 800ft for the final approach. 'Give us 2,300' he asks Beard, who increases the rpm on the propeller pitch levers. Herring pushes up the manifold pressure to 38in; this is a safety factor in case they have to 'go around'. Herring drops the nose and calls for wing flaps to be lowered a third of their travel while he cuts off the auto pilot. There is more vibration on the rudder pedals but it is not excessive. The airspeed indicator is indicating 130 IAS. At 500ft Herring calls 'Full flap!' Beard switches the control to the limit. Herring pulls back the throttles and calls 'High rpm!' Beard moves the pitch controls. The runway approaches fast. Over the threshold

Below:
Flaps fully down on final: crossing the threshold by the flying control van at the runway head.

Herring eases back on the control column and *The Iron Ass* settles. A jolt, a judder and smoke flies as the main wheels make contact with the concrete. The tail settles and the aircraft judders again as the tail-wheel touches. *The Iron Ass* is home at 1621hrs — seven hours and nine minutes after departing the same runway.

Herring lets the aircraft roll the length of the runway, only applying the brakes once speed has diminished to about 25mph. He watches that the hydraulic pressure is held. Beard opens the engine cowl flaps fully to cool engines — it also has a slowing effect. He turns off the turbos, booster pumps and generators.

'Tail wheel!' Herring calls, and Beard unlocks it. Herring turns right on to the perimeter track while Beard raises the flaps. Herring signals to Beard to cut the inboard engines and Beard moves the mixture controls to 'Idle Cut-Off'. The two outboard engines will be used to manoeuvre the bomber while taxying.

The Chief and his assistant are waiting with chocks and place them as soon as Herring brings the aircraft to a halt. The parking brake is not applied, to let the heat dissipate from the drums. The pilots turn off all electrical switches, the battery and master last to prevent arcing of relays. The control column is moved, pulled forward, the rudder pedals centralised and the lock handle pulled up. The aileron lock is also put in place.

The gunners in the rear of the aircraft have not waited to remove their guns, but have tumbled out of the door to view the tail damage. A six-foot high hole meets their gaze. A small crowd has gathered. Chuck Haywood climbs on to the tailplane to get a closer look. The

Top right:
The crew disembarks and spectators arrive as another Fortress taxies in.

Right:
Chuck Haywood can hardly believe his eyes: 'I'd have been very worried if I'd known that much of the tail was gone'.

large extent of the hole has been caused by the airflow tearing surface skin. The pilots drop out of the nose hatch. The Chief hands Herring the Form 1 and 1A to complete. 'What you been doing to my ship, Lieutenant?' he offers the standard joke.

'Thought it needed a little perforation', Herring replies with a grin.

'That's a hangar job for the sheet metal boys. You won't be flying this one for a few days.'

The Group CO has arrived to view the damage. The gunners remove their guns and place them in the back of the 6 × 6 truck which has arrived, and then climb in after them. The guns will be deposited at the armoury for cleaning after interrogation. They are tired and hungry, but happy to cross another mission off their tour. *The Iron Ass* has served them well today.

Four days later Roger Dearmon and Charles Haywood were 'commandeered' to fly with another crew whose ball and tail gunners had been wounded. The bomber never returned. Eight days after that the rest of the Herring crew failed to return from a mission to Berlin when the B-17F they were flying developed severe mechanical trouble and fell victim to fighters. The crew all baled out successfully, five becoming PoWs and the others managing to make contact with the Resistance, who befriended them. Repaired, The Iron Ass was taken out by another crew four days after Herring and his men went down. It did not return.

Right:
Another view of the man-sized hole in *The Iron Ass*, alias 42-39988 QJ:A.

Below:
B-17F 42-30071 which flew with 'A' Group on the raid described, was later transferred to another squadron and had to crash land at Honington depot when the landing gear could not be lowered. It was not repaired.

Far right:
Nose art of 96th Bomber Group B-17s on the mission covered. *Stingy*, leadship of 'B' Group.

Top right:
The Reluctant Dragon 42-38133, AW:O flew in the lead squadron of 'A' Group.

Right:
Ole Puss 42-30070, MI:U, was in the low squadron of 'A' Group.

Below left:
Mischief Maker II 42-30412, QJ:B, was also in the 'A' Group low squadron. The Herring crew were lost in this aircraft on their 15th mission.

Below right:
Stormy Weather 42-31621, BX:R, brought up the rear of the lead squadron 'B' Group.

Bottom left:
Back to work. The Chief, Floyd Franklin, checks spark plug leads after installing a new engine.

Bottom right:
Corporal Robert Apperson, mechanic in the Franklin ground crew, tightens a union on the same engine.

42

Comparison with Contemporaries

Assessing the worth of a bomber aircraft by comparison with its contemporaries is difficult for, unlike fighters, they did not compete one type against another. The very conception of fighter design is to achieve superiority over opposing fighter types; whereas bomber design has the aim of surviving in a hostile environment to deliver ordnance for the destruction of ground targets.

Different requirements in the scale and nature of destructive force, together with varying operational methods of achieving the desired goal, resulted in wide divergence in bomber design. Thus in World War 2, size came to be the distinguishing factor and bombers were broadly classified into light, medium,

Below:
The first Flying Fortress, Boeing Model 299, on a test flight.

heavy and very heavy categories. Tactical needs, however, brought different roles and design developments that blurred these classifications.

The B-17 Fortress was ostensibly designed as a long-range maritime reconnaissance bomber during a period when the US government pursued an isolationist policy and when military expenditure was only acceptable for defence purposes. With a change of administration, and faced with the expansionist policies of Nazi Germany and Japan, the B-17 became the aircraft around which the USAAC's doctrine of daylight precision bombing was developed. With intelligence gained from the early months of air fighting in Europe, the B-17 was redesigned to enhance its defensive firepower and give it better high altitude stability to provide a more stable bomb sighting platform. In contrast to the bomber designs of other belligerents, the B-17 was tailored to operate in the sub-stratosphere altitudes of 20,000 to 30,000ft, and in daylight. An effective turbo-supercharging of engines, an excellent crew oxygen supply system and an accurate high altitude bombsight were crucial elements in this development. The tactical considerations being that the higher the altitude the less effective anti-aircraft artillery would be against the bomber, and intercepting fighters would also have difficulties, notably the heavy drain on fuel in climbing to reach these heights, severely limiting their endurance.

In contrast, the heavy bombers developed for the Royal Air Force were expected to operate mainly under cover of darkness and at much lower altitudes. The German Luftwaffe was originally

Boeing B-17G Fortress

Handley-Page Halifax

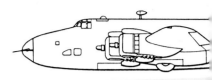

	Empty weight – pounds
B-17G	36 135
Halifax	38 240
P.108B	38 183
Stirling	45 000
Pe-8	36 728
B-24J	36 500
Lancaster	36 900
He 177A	37 038

Empty weight – pounds.

	Normal internal fuel capacity
	2810
	2628
	3273
	2705
	4117
	2814
	2585
	2537

Normal internal fuel capacity –
US gallons.

Short Stirling 1

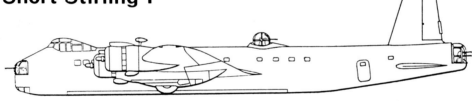

	Total horsepower
B-17G	4800
Halifax	6430
P.108B	5920
Stirling	6360
Pe-8	5400
B-24J	4800
Lancaster	5500
He 177A	5900

Total horsepower available for
take-off.

	Service ceiling
	35 600
	24 000
	19 685
	20 500
	25 920
	28 000
	24 500
	25 250

Service ceiling – feet

Consolidated B-24J Liberator

Avro Lancaster

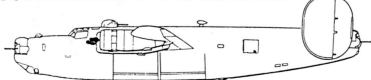
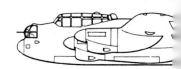

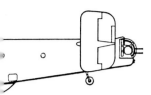

Piaggio P.108B

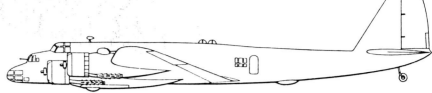

Range

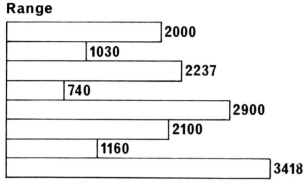

2000	
1030	
2237	
740	
2900	
2100	
1160	
3418	

Load

5000	
	13 000
2205	
	14 000
4400	
5000	
	14 000
4400	

Bomb load/Range: Range in miles carrying quoted bomb load in pounds.

Petlyakov Pe-8 (TB-7)

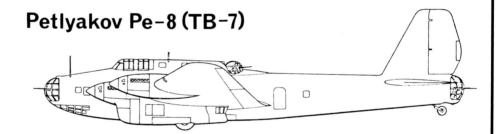

Il aircraft profiles are to the same scale.

50 feet

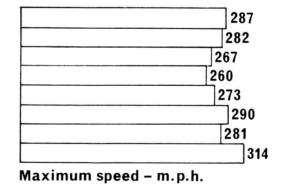

287	
282	
267	
260	
273	
290	
281	
314	

Maximum speed – m.p.h.

Heinkel He 177A-5

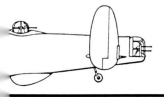

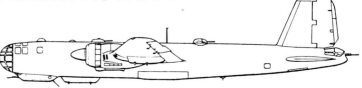

created to support land forces and was thus largely a tactical air arm. German interest in long range heavy bombers was limited and only one model in this classification entered service, but others were under development before the end of hostilities. Luftwaffe bombers of the early war years were in the twin-engined light or medium classification. The Russians too, were primarily interested in air support for their ground forces although a few four-engined bombers were produced. The Japanese, like their Axis partners, concentrated on employing air power in support of army and navy operations. A solitary four-motor heavy bomber design was produced but never reached quantity production.

The only operational bomber similarly tasked to the B-17 was its running mate in the strategic bombing campaign over Europe, the Consolidated B-24 Liberator. A later design by four years the Liberator embodied some of the new developments in aircraft engineering and equipment. However, the B-17 was more suited to the type of operations undertaken by the USAAF, primarily because it had better high altitude performance. A loaded B-17G was a relatively stable aircraft, even at 25,000ft, and was not difficult to control at 30,000ft. A fully loaded B-24J, on the other hand, required constant pilot attention to maintain position in formation at 20,000ft — at 25,000ft it was

floundering. The characteristics of the B-24's high aspect ratio wing were not suited to flight in thin air while supporting a heavy load. Above 18,000ft the B-24 became progressively demanding of the pilot on the controls as altitude increased, while the Fortress presented no detrimental change until over 30,000ft. However, at lower altitude most pilots with experience of both bombers considered the B-24 easier to handle. Both types had turbo-supercharged engines but the B-24 used the Pratt & Whitney 1830 whereas the B-17 had the longer stroked Wright 1820. The 1830 showed slightly better reliability and did not use — or disgorge — oil to the same extent as the Wright. The take-off horsepower rating of 1,200 was the same for the two makes so the B-24's slightly better performance can be attributed to cleaner aerodynamic design.

Below:

The original B-17 design featured a completely different empenage and rear fuselage. The Fortress I (B-17C) was the model with which the RAF initiated B-17 operations in the summer of 1941. AM519 is seen shortly after delivery across the Atlantic. It went to the Aircraft & Armament Experimental Establishment at Farnborough. (The 20 aircraft in this batch were erroneously serialled AM518-AM537 and later re-numbered AN518-AN537).

Both the B-17 and the B-24 had bomb bays taking the full depth of the fuselage with a crew walkway through the centre. The B-24's bay was divided into a front and rear section which together provided almost double the room of that in the B-17. However, the design of the bay and racks limited the largest size of individual bomb to 2,000lb, of which the Fortress could carry two and the Liberator four. With combinations of smaller bombs the load could be substantially increased particularly with the slim 1,600lb armour piercing bombs, of which the B-17 could accommodate six (9,600lb) and the B-24 eight (12,800lb). If under-wing racks were used heavier bombs could be lifted, but these very heavy loads brought flight stability difficulties.

In practice, tactical considerations — range and altitude — were the influencing factors and average bomb loads for the B-17 and B-24 in the USAAF high altitude daylight operations were 5,000lb and 6,000lb respectively. In operations over Europe, to reach more distant targets, loads were often 1,000lb less than the average. The heaviest operational load known lifted by a B-17 was two 4,500lb Disney rocket bombs on under-wing racks and this demanded caution at the flight controls. The racks were used to supplement bomb bay loads when attacking short range targets, but the effect upon high altitude climb through the increased fuel consumption

Above:
The Fortress I's hand-held guns were found totally inadequate for defence by the men of No 90 Squadron RAF. Even so the gunners on this aircraft, AN530, shot down the first enemy fighter to fall to a Fortress.

Left:
The contrast between the big tailed Fortress and the earlier configuration is well illustrated in this mixed formation of B-17D and B-17E models operating from Hawaii early in 1942.

Below left:
An early Douglas-built B-17G on final approach. The Fortress was the only USAAF bomber of World War 2 seeing extensive service that did not have a tricycle undercarriage. The retraction mechanism was electrically operated with mechanical back-up and proved fairly hardy. W. Larkins

at high engine temperatures limited their use.

At similar loadings and at the same altitude the maximum speeds of the B-17G and the B-24J were much alike, 280mph and 290mph at 25,000ft. The difference in combat cruise speed was more marked; 208 true airspeed for the B-17G as against 220 for the B-24J at 20,000ft, due to the slightly higher power settings required by the B-24. This difference in airspeed was sufficient to make it undesirable to fly the two types in adjacent formations.

When it came to range with the same amount of fuel and the same altitude, the B-24 could achieve up to 200 miles more than the B-17. Both aircraft had provision for additional fuel tanks in the bomb bay which would add an additional 1,000 miles to range. The larger bomb bay of the B-24 still allowed for a reasonable bomb load, whereas in the B-17 this was seriously curtailed. It was for this reason that the B-24 was the preferred type for maritime patrols or in the Pacific war zones where much greater distances than in Europe had to be flown on combat missions.

Range considerations were the principal reason for the B-24 replacing B-17s in the Pacific. In Europe the reverse was the case. The Fortress's better high altitude behaviour found it the more favoured type with USAAF commanders. The B-17's excellent flight characteristics, the foremost being directional stability with little requirement for trim, made it far more suited to survive damage than the B-24. Several Fortresses were landed successfully with complete tail stabilisers shot off and major damage to wings. B-24s were in general less able to keep flying with comparable damage to flight surfaces.

When comparing the B-17 with the three major British four-engined bombers, the most striking difference is the maximum bomb loads. The Short Stirling, earliest of the British designs, could accommodate and lift 14,000lb, the Handley Page Halifax 13,000lb, and the Avro Lancaster 14,000lb. The more extensive bomb bays in the British aircraft, in contrast to the B-17 and B-24, only occupied the fuselage area below the wing spar and were not encumbered by walkways. This allowed the carriage of more bombs, and in the case of the Halifax and Lancaster larger bombs, with 4,000lb bombs being dropped regularly by Lancasters. Much larger bombs were also carried and modified Lancasters dropped 41 special 22,000lb deep penetration missiles.

The normal maximum loads of the British bombers could only be carried some 750 miles at operational altitude by the Stirling, 1,000 miles by the Halifax and 1,500 miles by the Lancaster. Loads were substantially reduced for long ranges but Lancasters and Halifaxes regularly hauled 10,000 to 12,000lb loads to the Ruhr and 8,000lb loads to Berlin. Unlike the USAAF day bombers, RAF heavies operating at night did not circle to gain altitude before setting course to penetrate enemy airspace. Normally the British heavies made their ascent during the run up to the enemy coast. The Stirling could not operate with a combat load at much above 15,000ft and the Halifax Mks I and II above 18,000ft. The radial engined Halifax Mk II did operate successfully at 20,000ft, which was also the optimum level for Lancaster sorties. The B-17G had better range than the Stirling and Halifax and marginally better than the Lancaster while flying at similar altitudes. All the British bombers had, on average, double the payload for similar ranges but the Lancaster's larger fuel load allowed it, even with a 10,000lb load, to match the B-17 on radius of action.

In the matter of armament differences the B-17G had much superior firepower to the British bombers: 13 .50in calibre machine guns to the usual eight .303in machine guns in three power turrets of British bombers. Moreover, the US .50 weapon had a higher muzzle velocity and much more destructive power than the rifle calibre weapons which defended the RAF bombers. To improve matters Lancasters of one Bomber Command group had two .50s as tail turret armament during the final months of hostilities. The British bombers did not have underside defences and were very

Below and Right:
The Fortress's docility, particularly when not laden for war, found it popular with high ranking officers as personal transport. B-17Gs were taken to the Pacific expressly for this purpose in 1945. That used by General George Kennedy had chin and ball turret removed, retaining only the tail, top turret and cheek armament. Seating was fitted at the waist windows which were hung with curtains! B-17G 44-83259 used by Gen Carl Spaatz and named for his daughter, had all armament removed. Below the co-pilot's window on both Fortresses was painted a red flash with four stars to indicate their VIP status.
via S. Birdsall & R. Besecker

vulnerable to attack from that quarter, albeit that in any event an approach from below by an interceptor could rarely be seen at night. In fact, the difficulty of being alerted to an enemy fighter's presence in any quarter during darkness was the greatest problem of bomber defence. Fortresses were experimentally employed on night operations, but the limitations on bomb load made such sorties uneconomical. By daylight the precision that could be achieved and the mass formation drops employed were proven means of using the type successfully.

Lancasters and Halifaxes frequently took part in daylight bombing of Ruhr targets during the final year of the war, by which time the Luftwaffe was in demise and fighter escort was provided to and from the target. Formations were much looser than those of the USAAF and target sighting was performed from individual aircraft. Attack altitudes were generally lower than those of the US heavies – 15,000ft to 18,000ft. Each of the British bombers delivered a more destructive load, and in practice this was more scattered than the formation drops of the B-17s and the B-24s.

The enemy air arms had no plans for strategic bombing forces prior to hostilities, air power being centred on support of army and navy operations. The Luftwaffe's sole heavy bomber to go

into service was the Heinkel He177 *Greif*. Of similar dimensions to the B-17 and the other Allied four-engined bombers, it had the novel feature of two coupled liquid cooled engines in one nacelle driving a single large propeller on each wing with the aim of minimising drag. This proved to be the weak feature of the design as the He177 was plagued by recurrent engine overheating problems that took the best part of three years to resolve.

In comparison with the B-17G, a much older design, the He177A had a lower operational altitude – around 15,000ft – against the B-17's 25,000ft. The service ceiling of the Heinkel was 25,250ft against the Fortress's 35,600ft. The He177's maximum speed was 314mph at 20,000ft, some 25mph higher than the B-17G at the same altitude, chiefly due to far more powerful engines. The Heinkel could lift ordnance loads as heavy as the British bombers, but much of this had to be carried externally. The normal operational load was only 4,480lb (2,000kg) although this corresponded with that of the Fortress on very long range flights; but even so it was able to haul this load some 500 miles further than the Fortress could at 20,000ft. The He177 flew at night during its limited bomber operations over Britain and the USSR but was also used in a long-range anti-shipping role. The defensive arma-

ment was good, albeit nowhere as extensive as the B-17Gs, but on some versions it included two 20mm cannon.

The Japanese did not produce a modern four-engined heavy bomber until 1944 and this type never entered service. The only other four-engined heavy bomber to be employed operationally by the Axis air arms was the Italian Piaggio P108B. First flown in November 1939, this type was of similar configuration to the early B-17 and is said to have had excellent handling characteristics. But the aircraft proved to be mechanically unreliable and production was curtailed after only 26 had been completed. Nevertheless, during 1942 and 1943 the only unit of the Italian Air Force equipped with the P108B did undertake 29 operational sorties. However, during these operations five of the bombers were shot down and three lost through mechanical failure or accident.

Compared with the B-17G, the P108B had a much lower operational altitude range, 15,000ft being the optimum with a service ceiling of 20,000ft. Its top speed was also some 20mph slower than that of the B-17G at 15,000ft despite higher rated engines. With a normal bomb load of 2,205lb (1,000kg) the Piaggio's range was approximately the same as the Fortress's. The Piaggio had a greater maximum internal load

Above:
**The ultimate Flying Fortress: gear
starting to lower, a late production B-17G
prepares to land. The defensive
armament shows well in this
photograph.** H. Holmes

capacity amounting to 7,716lb
(3,500kg) for short range flight but the
engine difficulties precluded such heavy
lifts on operations. An advanced feature
of the P108B was the two remote
controlled twin machine gun barbettes
mounted at the rear of each outboard
engine nacelle and sighted from stations
on the fuselage. A single machine gun in
a retractable 'dustbin' type turret provided underside defence but this was
both cumbersome and considered in-
effective. Overall the seven or eight
machine gun defensive armament was
vastly inferior to the B-17G's but, in
fairness, this bomber was more the
contemporary of the B-17F model than
the G, even though in the matter of
comparison the same judgements apply.

One other four-engined bomber of
World War 2 is worthy of comparison
with the Fortress, particularly as,
unlike those already mentioned, it was
of similar vintage, having first flown in
1936. This is the Petlyakov Pe-8, which
was orginally known by the Soviet
bomber designation T-7 until that
system was dropped in favour of ack-
nowledging the leader of the design
team responsible for an aircraft. Most of
the total of 79 Pe-8s reputed to have been
completed were on hand before the
German invasion of the USSR in August

1941, but the type remained in service
until the end of hostilities. During the
war years many Pe-8s were extensively
modified and re-engined – once with
diesels to enable these bombers to attack
Berlin.

In comparison with the B-17G the Pe-8
was a slightly larger and more powerful
aircraft, an auxiliary engine in the
fuselage provided supercharging that
enabled the Pe-8 to be operated at
between 20,000ft and 25,000ft. At this
altitude its maximum speed was some
20mph below the B-17G's. Maximum
range with a 4,408lb (2,000kg) bomb
load was 2,900 miles at a speed of
174mph with fuel overload amounting
to a massive 4,120US gal. Bomb load
could be doubled but this severely
curtailed range and altitude performance. The B-17 could only equal or
better this range by using bomb bay fuel
tanks which then reduced its payload to
2,000lb.

The armament of the Pe-8 featured a
20mm cannon in the nose, tail and
dorsal turrets, all manually manipulated, and a single machine gun in
manned emplacements at the rear of
each engine nacelle. Although heavier
weapons were employed, the Pe-8 was
less well defended than the B-17, particularly as the US type's power turrets
were far superior in operation to those
on the Russian aircraft. The Pe-8, like
the other non-US bombers, operated
chiefly at night with a view to improving
its chances of survival in hostile airspace.

Overall, it can be stated that the B-17G
had a superior high-altitude performance to all other Allied and Axis
bombers. In maximum speed the only
notably faster bomber was the He177. In
tactical speeds the Fortress was similar
to its contemporaries except when flying
in formation where uniformity
demanded lower power settings. The
B-17G's range was better than that of the
British heavies, equal to the Piaggio but
less than the Pe-8 and the He177 with
similar bomb loads. In the matter of
maximum loads it was at the bottom of
the scale, but only marginally so except
in comparison with the British bombers.
In the case of defensive armament the
B-17 justified the name Fortress, for in
number of guns, calibre and effectiveness it was the best armed, with the
B-24 running a close second.

If cautiously loaded, the B-17G had no
really undesirable flight characteristics
and was a pilot-forgiving aircraft, easy
to fly. While it is extremely doubtful if
any one pilot had experience of all the
types reviewed it appears that, with the
exception of the Lancaster and Liberator, the other types left something to be
desired in mechanical ability or operation. Opinions from those who have
flown Lancaster, Liberator and Fortress
single out the last named as the less
demanding, even at low and medium
altitudes. Some measure of the B-17's
popularity with pilots can be found in
the number of these bombers that were
adapted for civil use in the years
following World War 2.

3
Combat Development

Most of the non-combat operational problems with the B-17 were as a result of operating at altitudes above an arbitary 20,000ft. Flying in the rarified air of the stratosphere presents no problems to the jet turbine propelled and pressurised aircraft of the latter half of the 20th century. For World War 2 aircraft powered by propeller-driven internal combustion engines, operating at such heights — even at the lower levels — was demanding on engines, airframe and crew.

The Fortress was adapted for high altitude flight to meet a US AAC concept for strategic bombing. The attraction of operating in the stratosphere was that the bombers would fly high enough to be above the range of most anti-aircraft artillery and that fighter interception would be difficult. For some years the AAC had been developing an automatic crew oxygen supply system, essential for high altitude flight, and turbo-supercharging to provide the necessary volume of air to sustain engine operation in the rarified atmosphere. Essential to the success of such a venture was an accurate high altitude bombsight which was available through a remarkable piece of computing apparatus designed by N. L. Norden for the US Navy. Turbo-superchargers installed in the limited production B-17B of 1938 enabled the aircraft to operate up to 30,000ft, at a time when other air forces were operating at levels below 12,000ft. With the following B-17C and B-17D models, the turbo-supercharging and oxygen systems were further refined and, using the Norden sight, some extraordinarily accurate bombing was achieved from heights of 20,000ft and more over ranges in the United States.

Although adapted rather than designed for sub-stratospheric flight, the early model Fortresses operated quite successfully from 20,000ft to 30,000ft apart from a pronounced loss of directional stability as altitude mounted. To operate from even higher levels — which was desirable from a defensive viewpoint — it was evident that lateral stability would have to be improved to provide the steady bombing platform that was necessary for precision sighting on targets. At the same time, in the light of day bomber operations during the first year of hostilities in Europe, it became clear that the current B-17 models were deficient in rearward facing armament, the area at which the

majority of fighter attacks were directed. In the five years since the B-17 first flew, there had been significant developments in military aviation and the type was moving towards obsolescence. As a result, an extensive redesign was undertaken that might well have warranted a completely new designation for the aircraft, so marked were the changes. The aft section beyond the trailing edge of the wing was completely redesigned. An extended fuselage with a position for tail guns was graced by a much larger empennage, notably a distinctive curving vertical stabiliser, which led to the popular description of the new Fortress as "the big-tailed bird'.

Officially designated as the B-17E, this first big-tailed model gave excellent handling coupled with good altitude stability. It was soon superseded in production by the B-17F which was the refined, war-worthy version. However, the big-tailed Fortress introduced a substantial increase in weight over its predecessors, 34,000lb against 27,000lb empty weight. The additional weight mitigated against high altitude performance and reduced the service ceiling. Also, the extended rear fuselage and larger empennage moved the centre of gravity rearwards. This required care in loading the aircraft, particularly in the aft section where, if heavily weighted, the Centre of Gravity (C of G) could be pushed beyond the 35% of the Mean Aerodynamic Chord point, increasing stalling speed and requiring increased power settings. In turn this meant higher fuel consumption to combat the general instability produced. For facilitating determination of the C of G, every individual B-17 was furnished with a Load Adjuster, a slide rule that enabled individual weight distribution to be computed, enabling crews to avoid precarious loadings. Apart from the redesign of the rear section of the B-17, extra weight came through the installation of power turrets and all the trappings necessary for combat operations. The doubling up of some systems and components to improve the chance of survival in battle also added to the increased load. This, of course, was common to many warplanes, but particularly so with those US designs originating in the prewar years where little or no account had been taken of the need for armour, self-sealing fuel tanks and much other equipment deemed

necessary for combat operations by the European belligerents.

There was another aspect of the weight situation. Two other sources of B-17 production were set up in California during 1941-42 involving different manufacturers, Douglas and Lockheed-Vega. Although supplied with design and production plans by Boeing to build the same model as the Seattle plant, the airframes and equipment differed in several respects. Douglas-built B-17Fs had strengthened mid-wing sections embracing the engine nacelles and these added approximately 450lb to the basic empty weight. Vega also used the same wing centre section design as Douglas but additionally strengthened part of the fuselage for a total extra weight of approximately 750lb. Apart from giving Vega B-17Fs a different flight attitude, it caused stress concentrations around the radio room where the rear fuselage was bolted to the forward section of the bomb bay. This led to a general preference among combat pilots for Boeing-built aircraft which were reckoned to have slightly better performance and handling qualities.

The weight increase in successive models of the Fortress would not have been such a matter of concern but for the mode of air warfare that the USAAF chose to pursue with its bombers. Asembling the large defensive bombing formations necessitated much orbiting and dog-leg courses, added to which the bombers had to be at or near operational altitude before penetration of hostile airspace. All this could consume an average two hours from the time of take-off to the final assembly over friendly territory. As atmospheric pressure decreased, so the rate of climb at a given power setting fell off, resulting in a prolonged climb making heavy inroads into fuel and thus reducing radius of action. As the original B-17F normally carried a maximum of 1,730US gal while the contemporary B-24D shouldered 2,364gal, the Fortress was quite clearly lacking range for the strategic bombing campaign planned by the USAAF. Indeed, the limited range of the B-17 in comparison with the B-24 was the major reason for the decision taken in 1942 to withdraw Fortresses from the Pacific war fronts in favour of the Liberator. And this was in an area where, unlike Europe, bombers could usually gain altitude during the long over-water flights to targets providing longer endurance.

Boeing's answer to the range problem was to place fuel cells in the outer wing sections of the B-17F — 18 in total. They added another 1,080US gal and substantially increased endurance. To make some compensation for the weight of the rubber composition cells and plumbing, the engine fire extinguishers were removed in the belief that the CO_2 system would be vulnerable to gunfire and thus a hazard to engine operation! By this and other economies the basic weight was kept to 35,728lb although when the extra fuel capacity was taken up it added another ton to the gross load. The fire extinguisher deletion was met with amazement by combat crews who had experiences of engine fires being doused

Left:
What could happen to an engine when a propeller failed to feather. This 390th Bomb Group aircraft was able to land safely after the wildly windmilling propeller had wrenched itself free.

Below:
The 8th Air Force had the North Sea and the English Channel to contend with when returning from operations, while the 15th Air Force had the Austrian Alps. With some parts over 10,000ft high it was an anxious time for a crew struggling home with an engine disabled. These 97th Bomb Group B-17Gs have everything going well and several thousand feet of airspace between them and the peaks.

by the system. Unfortunately it was easier to delete items in production than reinstate them, and a year elapsed before B-17s with engine fire extinguisher rings were again reaching combat groups in Europe.

Another deletion associated with weight saving that had far reaching operational effects concerned the propeller feathering mechanism. Feathering — turning the blades so that they are at 90° to the drive shaft with the leading edge fully forward to bring a propeller to a standstill — was essential if an engine failed. If a propeller was in cutting pitch without the braking effect of an engine under power, it could 'windmill' and build up revolutions to a point where extreme and dangerous vibration would occur. Often a runaway propeller turned so fast that the drive shaft or engine reduction housing broke, causing the propeller to fly off and slash into the fuselage, wing or another engine.

The feathering system in the B-17 featured an electrically actuated hydraulic pump in each engine nacelle using oil from the engine lubrication tank. On early B-17s there was a standpipe in the oil tank holding a reserve of oil for feathering, but with a redesigned and increased capacity oil tank the standpipe was deleted to reduce the weight of the new component. So long as there was oil in the tank the propeller feathered, but it was found that if, during an engine failure, the sump was fractured or the oil supply quickly lost through some other breakage, the propeller feathering system failed to work. In combat, when engines sustained damage and had to be shut down, the numbers of failures to feather propellers became particularly pronounced. But the full extent of this problem was not appreciated until a survey of the cause of aircraft loss was conducted, late in 1944, among incapacitated prisoners of war who had been repatriated. Of 150 B-17s lost, inability to feather a propeller had been a direct or a contributory cause in 70 cases. In late production B-17Gs a stand pipe was again fitted in the oil tank and other Fortresses already in service had their fuel tanks modified to include this feature, but the refitting programme was not completed before the end of hostilities.

There were some 200 detailed changes during the course of B-17F production, generally introduced on the assembly line several at one time and signified by a so-called block number. The B-17G was, in effect, a continuation of this policy but the significant introduction of a powered nose gun turret decided the authorities to bestow a new model designation. In fact, the chin turret was first introduced on 86 Douglas-built B-17Fs of blocks 70, 75 and 80 which were redesignated as B-17Gs after delivery to the USAAF. With the G model

empty weight climbed to 36,135lb, although once more an attempt was made to minimise the increase by deleting fixtures or equipment that were then considered dispensable. Armour plate was a prime target for these economies and that secured to the bulkhead between the pilots and the nose compartment went on the first B-17Gs produced. Early in production the surrounding armour at the rear waist gunners' stations was also deleted. The C of G situation remained much the same and use had to be made of elevator trim tabs to counter the tail-heavy flight attitude, action which was estimated to rob the B-17G of about 10mph.

Several other deletions and changes were made on B-17G production to further reduce weight, especially in the rear section, but this only amounted to a few hundred pounds. More effect was obtained by the measures adopted in combat groups from the spring of 1944 when actions with enemy fighters were on the wane. Analysis of action at the various B-17 gun stations showed that the radio room hatch gun was rarely fired, chiefly because the gunner seldom saw the approach of enemy fighters. In general, the hand-held guns in nose and waist were the least effective due to the difficulty in accurate sighting. The two waist gunners very rarely opened fire at the same time and also had difficulty in seeing the approach of enemy aircraft. As a result, the 8th Air Force's 1st Division recommended the complete removal of the radio room gun and use of only one gunner to man both waist guns. As a result of the frequent combats between enemy aircraft and US bombers during 1943 and the following winter, it became usual to carry several extra boxes of .50in ammunition above the amount usually specified for the waist and tail guns, the additional ammunition being lodged in the radio room. A stricter policy forbade this additional supply and halved the ammunition usually carried for the waist guns. In total some 400lb was removed or relocated with the benefit of bringing the C of G forward several inches. In the final months of hostilities some B-17 units experimented with eliminating the waist guns completely while others removed the chin and ball turrets. This much improved the C of G factor and also gave another 25mph at cruise settings.

The worst aspect of high altitude flight was the very low temperatures which affected both men and equipment. In Europe this was aggravated by the high moisture content of the atmosphere so that icing was a constant hazard. Unless protective measures were taken, bomb bay doors, bomb shackles, machine gun breeches and other equipment froze up. Additionally, hydraulically operated systems were sluggish because of a thickening of the oil through exposure to sub-zero tem-

peratures. Notorious were the turbo-supercharger regulators which were hydraulically operated. Unless these were regularly exercised — running the turbo through its range and then back again — the oil congealed to a point where control was completely lost. This precipitated overspeeding of the turbine — popularly called a bucket wheel — and could lead to its disintegration. The supercharger turbine regulator operated the waist gate, a flap in the exhaust outlet that controlled the amount of exhaust gas force applied to drive the bucket wheel. Supercharger failure at high altitude produced a critical situation as, without pressurised air to feed into the engine manifold, the required power could not be obtained. An aircraft so stricken could not keep up with the rest of the formation and would straggle, to become easy prey to enemy fighters. Pilots had to constantly monitor supercharger speed at high altitude and make frequent adjustments to the turbo controls.

Soon after the B-17G entered production electronically operated turbo regulators replaced the hydraulic type. The new regulators had a simple switch on the pilots' consul which controlled all four turbos, the setting selected being automatically maintained. The electronic regulators won immediate and universal acclaim from B-17 pilots. Lt-Col Immanual Klette, who flew 91 combat missions in B-17s, a total greater than any other 8th Air Force pilot, considered electronic turbo controls the most important and beneficial of all improvements made to the B-17 for combat operations. The first aircraft reaching Europe with the new regulators were from Douglas and Vega in October 1943. They did not appear on Boeing B-17Gs sent to the 8th and 15th Air Forces until two months later. Following close behind electronic regulators was an uprated turbo-supercharger with a high speed turbine wheel. The higher speed produced greater air compression and raised the B-17G's critical altitude by some 4,000ft.

Throughout production, the B-17F and B-17G were powered with the same model engines, the Wright R-1820-97 Cyclone rated at 1,200hp. A nine-cylinder air-cooled radial design, the engine adapted well to turbo-supercharging and proved very reliable. In addition to production from the Wright plant, it was also manufactured by the Studebaker Corporation, an automotive company whose engines initially went to B-17Fs built by Vega and Douglas. In combat units it soon became apparent that the Studebaker engines were not as reliable as those from Wright, and if there was any choice pilots would select an aircraft that did not have Studebaker engines. Eventually there was nothing to choose between production from either source.

In addition to the manufacturers' development of the Fortress to meet combat exigencies and operating environment, there were the special needs of the two main combat theatres, the United Kingdom and Italy, involving modifications. At depots in England, Italy and North Africa, a pre-combat modification programme involved as many as 40 items, although this fluctuated considerably with each passing month. Most modifications concerned armament and accessories deemed necessary from combat experience. Although the number of theatre modifications declined towards the end of hostilities the B-17, as received from the United States, always required some refinement.

As became its name, Flying Fortress, the B-17 carried the heaviest defensive armament of any World War 2 bomber that saw extensive operational service. The six .50s and one .30 flexible guns of the B-17C and B-17D were increased to one .30 and eight .50s in the B-17E, first big-tail model Fortress, of which four .50s were in powered turrets. B-17Fs went from nine to 12 guns, dispensing with the .30 nose weapon early in the production run. The B-17G went from 11 to 13 .50s and then to 12 when the radio room gun was deleted. In combat zones extra guns were installed; twin or single .50s in the nose to replace the .30s were first in evidence with units operating the Fortress in the southwest Pacific area during 1942. Similar installations were made in the United Kingdom, where the forward defences were also found inadequate to meet fighter attacks directed at the front quarter. Some 8th Air Force B-17Fs had 13 .50s, but most 12. A few of these bombers

placed on the exposed flanks of formations were experimentally fitted with twin waist guns, but the extra weight had a pronounced effect on handling qualities as the C of G was pushed rearward. Another combat improvisation was the fitting of a 20mm cannon in the nose transparency, but this proved difficult for the gunner to control and its recoil threatened to weaken the nose structure. Another experiment to improve frontal defences was the installation of a battery of six fixed .50s in a modified chin turret on a B-17G, fired by the pilot. The purpose of the installation was to meet the Luftwaffe mass fighter attacks, but an occasion never arose for this to be tested. The aircraft concerned, B-17G 42-31435 of the 384th Bomb Group, probably had the heaviest armament found on any B-17.

Fortress Armament

Left:
Waist or beam gun apertures on B-17C and B-17D were curved and dished into the tapering fuselage. The field of fire was far more limited than with the rectangular openings of the big tail Fortress models. This photograph shows a member of the RAF's No 90 Squadron working on a .50in calibre Browning which was the standard weapon installed at this position.

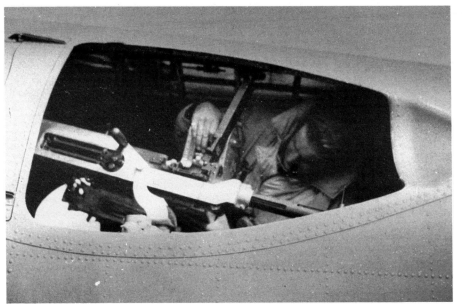

Below:
Both left and right-hand guns can be seen in the waist of this B-17E where the apertures were directly opposite one another. An early modification on the B-17F to give the gunners more room to manoeuvre and widen the angles of fire was the relocation of the gun mounts nearer the edge of the sill. Note the retracted wind deflectors forward of the window.

Right:
The relative stagger of the waist gun positions can be clearly seen in this photograph. This development was introduced on the production line with the Boeing Model B-17G-50-BO, the Douglas B-17G-25-DL and the Vega B-17G-50-VE. At the same time the windows were enclosed and a K-5 gun mount incorporated at the base. Douglas was the first to deliver Fortresses with these features but their original framed transparency gave way to the single clear sheet of Plexiglas common to all production sources.

Centre right:
To provide better gunner environment in the many Fortresses with open waist windows a standard three-panel glazed enclosure with K-5 mount was made available to modification centres. These structures were slightly bulged at the base to place the gun mount well out.

Below:
The first production B-17Es, like this photographed in India early in 1942, had a remotely controlled barbette ventral turret with two .50in Brownings. It was sighted by a periscope device in the clear bubble shaped transparency further back under the fuselage. Gunners found that it was extremely difficult to track an attacking fighter with this unit.
E. Walker

Top left and Bottom left:
In contrast, the ingenious manned ventral turret, that came to be called the ball, was an extremely effective gun position. The gunner made his entry from the fuselage after take-off, for it was no place to be in a crash. Cramped for the gunner, it was equally so for armourers carrying out servicing on the ground.

Above and Right:
'Tail Stinger' was the popular name for the twin .50in calibre machine gun position at the extreme rear of the fuselage of B-17E, F and early G models. The installation proved very effective against attacking fighters although the guns were limited to an all-round 60° movement. The remote ring and post sight was linked to the guns by a series of bell cranks. The gunner's body was protected by a large piece of armour plate, ⅜in thick.

Above:
The neater, lighter Cheyenne tail gun position provided a reflector sight and gave a greater field of fire through increasing gun movement in both azimuth and elevation to 90°. Introduced on factory production in the summer of 1944, many earlier B-17Gs had Cheyenne 'turrets' retro-fitted at modification centres. The 15th Air Force in particular, had such a programme and several older Fortresses like this B-17G-30-BO of the 2nd Bomb Group received a new rear end. Note the ball turret faces forward. It was the practice with some crews to have the ball turret gunner count the bombs out and report over the interphone that all had cleared.

Left:
The deficiency in forward armament of the B-17E and F brought a great variety of 'in the field' improvisations. The original .30in calibre machine gun was intended to be moved from one ball socket to another in the Plexiglas nosepiece, but this was found totally impractical in flight. The Australian-based 19th Bomb Group had two ball sockets placed in close proximity in the upper part of the nosepiece so that twin .30s could be mounted. The gunner — seen here in his seat — had to stand stooped to fire them. Note the disused ball socket.

Bottom and Right:
To further improve forward firepower some B-17s had three .50s in the nosepiece and a .30in in a side window on each side of the nose.

Bottom right:
B-17F 41-24440, one of three specially modified for high altitude photography work with the 15th Photo Mapping Squadron in North Africa (note camera ports at side and under nose), had two spaced .50s in reinforced and braced mounts in the upper Plexiglas nosepiece. Additionally, a .30 was fitted in the right lower nose ball socket and in each of two enlarged side windows. The array in the nose was possible as no bomb sight was carried.

Above:
A number of 8th Air Force B-17Fs were equipped with twin .50s in the upper part of the nose transparency. They carried no bomb sight and were usually placed to fly on the wing of the lead aircraft. *Geezil* 42-5404 was a 306th Bomb Group aircraft.

Left and right:
The side or cheek window gun positions were many and varied, originally being installed at modification centres and sometimes on combat airfields. When incorporated in production, Vega B-17Fs could be distinguished by the centre placing of the right-hand gun window and forward placing of the left – as on 385th BG's *Shack Bunny*, 42-5913. Boeing and Douglas had the opposite arrangement – as on 385th BG's *Piccadilly Queen*, 42-30251, and 388th BG's *Sweetheart*, 42-3262. An improved cheek position gave another 10° of gun movement towards the front. Two types – as on *Slo Joe*, 42-30168 of 385th BG and *Short Stuff*, 42-30332 of 390th BG – were fitted at modification centres in the US or UK. With the introduction of the B-17G with its chin turret a decision was made in the US to dispense with cheek guns and the first B-17s to reach England and Italy featured the original nose window layout – as *Blue Dreams*, 42-37761 of 91st BG.

Left:
Finally reinstated on production aircraft, the standardised location of cheek guns was left forward, giving 40° of gun movement in azimuth and 58° in elevation; and right back, giving 90° in azimuth and 68° in elevation.

Below:
An experimental installation of a 20mm cannon in a B-17F nose. Even though stoutly braced, the recoil was such that it threatened to weaken the nose structure.

Armament Diagram – Perspective

Above:
The layout of armament and armour
plate that was installed in the YB-40.
Excessive weight was its downfall.

Key:

1 Bendix lower retractable chin turret – 400 rounds per gun.
2 Sperry Model BT-44-UD-104 upper forward turret – 400 rounds per gun.
3 Martin Model 250CE4 upper rear turret – 400 rounds per gun.
4 Briggs lower semi-retractable turret – 600 rounds per gun.
5 USMC power-boosted twin .50 calibre side guns – 300 rounds per gun.
6 USMC power-boosted twin .50 calibre side guns – 550 rounds per gun.
7 Reserve ammunition for chin turret – 400 rounds per gun.
8 Reserve ammunition for upper forward turret – 400 rounds per gun.
9 Reserve ammunition for all stations – four 200 round boxes, twenty 150 round boxes.
10 Ammunition boxes for tail guns – 300 rounds per gun, 250 rounds per gun in tracks.
11 USMC hydraulic system for side guns.
12 USMC hydraulic system for tail guns.
13 Armour plate for crew protection.
14 Armour plate for power plant protection.

Top left and Bottom left:
The Sperry A-1 'top turret' gave 360° of movement in azimuth and could be elevated from 5° below the horizontal plane to 85° above. The two .50s were fed with 125 rounds each and a reserve magazine with another 125 for the two. The gunners' main complaint was due to restricted vision and thus the original metal side plates were replaced with clear panels on 8th Air Force aircraft.

Above:
Early in 1944 new B-17Gs were fitted with top turrets having a higher dome and more glazing, therefore affording the gunner better visibility. The new dome could be fitted to older turrets.
R. Armstrong

Right:
The Bendix chin turret guns could be moved through 172° in azimuth and 72° in elevation. Each of two magazines held 365 rounds. The reflector sight was suspended from the top rim of the nosepiece.

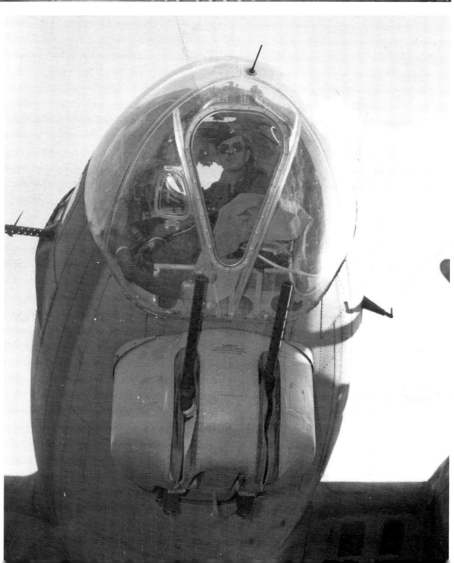

B-17G : Armament and zones of fire.

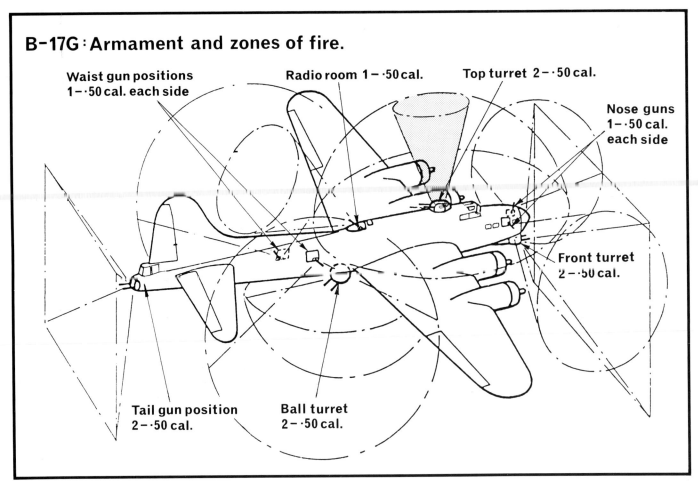

Waist gun positions
1 – ·50 cal. each side

Radio room 1 – ·50 cal.

Top turret 2 – ·50 cal.

Nose guns
1 – ·50 cal.
each side

Front turret
2 – ·50 cal.

Tail gun position
2 – ·50 cal.

Ball turret
2 – ·50 cal.

Above:
B-17G: armament and zones of fire.

The effect of the B-17's defensive armament was greatly exaggerated due to the high number of enemy aircraft claimed destroyed or damaged by gunners. While it was evident that several gunners in a bomber formation were all shooting at the same enemy aircraft and each claiming its destruction in good faith, the extent to which the speed of combat could delude individuals as to the outcome was not so readily appreciated. In consequence, although combat analysis experts were aware gunners' claims were greatly exaggerated, it was still believed that the B-17 and B-24 gunners were taking a far greater toll of the enemy fighter force than actually proved to be the case. Thus the heavier the defensive armament the greater the chance of survival appeared to be the rule to many observers. The realities of this belief was the failure of the YB-40, the designation given to a dozen B-17Fs modified as formation gunships and given an operational trial with the 8th Air Force in England during the summer of 1943. Carrying no bomb load, the standard B-17F defensive armament was supplemented by an additional power turret in the radio room position, twin waist guns and the first Bendix chin turrets seen on combat Fortresses. In total, 16 guns and approximately 15,000 rounds of ammu-

nition were carried. Positioned on the flanks of formations, the YB-40 was supposed to afford extra protection to the bombers. In practice it was more a liability than an asset as the heavy rear loading so altered the C of G, demanding excessive trim, that the B-17s had to reduce speed to enable the YB-40 to stay with them. It was soon realised that a YB-40 sortie was an uneconomical venture as it afforded little, if any, advantage in formation defence and did not deliver a bomb load.

More penetrating assessments of B-17 gunnery questioned the effectiveness of the hand-held weapons, particularly those in beam positions. While much depended on the skill of the individual, the general consensus of opinion was that for the average gunner obtaining strikes on enemy fighters it was a matter of luck. Such were the complexities of accurate aiming when both gun platform and target were moving at different speeds and directions, the USAAF settled on teaching what was termed a Zone System of firing. In effect this was pointing the gun in the direction of the target and filling that area of sky with bullets. The most effective positions were found to be the top and ball power turrets and the tail guns. The twin tail guns were manipulated by hand, but in the original installation they were limited to 30° movement either side of the vertical and horizontal plane. A redesign conducted by the modification centre at Cheyenne, Wyoming, provided 45° in

elevation and an improved sight — a reflector model — and gunner outlook. The revised turret was taken into production and featured on all new B-17Gs from the late summer of 1944.

Developments in respect of the B-17's ordnance load throughout the big-tail models were minimal. All-electric bomb releases, dispensing with the mechanical salvo mechanism, introduced during B-17G production in early 1944, proved in combat operation to be troublesome due to electrical failures. Underwing racks that could be installed and were capable of supporting 4,000lb bombs were little used as the additional drag and weight required more power to gain high altitude, depleting fuel resources. One wing of the 8th Air Force was fitted out to carry glide bombs on these under-wing racks. The glide bomb was simply a 1,000lb high explosive bomb with wings and empennage that could be released to glide down on a target, with the benefit that the delivering bombers could turn away before flying into a target area with heavy AA fire. Tried only once operationally, it was found inaccurate, as were the dropping of other under-wing loads. A further use of under-wing racks was to launch radio controlled stand-off bombs. Apart from the VB-1 Azon, a 1,000lb bomb with radio controlled tail fins, giving side-to-side directional changes which was used with some success in Italy, most of these weapons never went beyond the combat experimental stage.

Fortress Radars

Left:
An under-nose 'bathtub'-housed H2S derivative ground scanning radar was fitted on Fortress III (B-17G) used by the RAF for electronic countermeasures work.   J. Rabbets

Below:
The original location of radar ground scanners on USAAF B-17s was under the nose. Production versions settled on making this installation in the ball turret well; the scanner was partly retractable. Here it is seen fully extended as a 457th Bomb Group leadplane salvos its load of bombs and target smoke markers.

Below:
Fortresses used on anti-submarine
patrols were fitted with ASV (air-to-
surface vessel) search radar. The
distinctive antennae are seen projecting
from the nose and below each wing on
Fortress IIA, FK209, ex B-17E
ex-41-9203.

Above:
**A Fortress III, HB781 of No 220
Squadron RAF Coastal Command with
H2X radar in the fully retracted position.
This radar was adapted for ocean
scanning.**
Left:

Right:
**The antenna of the AN/APQ-7 Eagle
ground scanning radar was contained in
an aerofoil-shaped housing resembling a
stub wing and positioned below the
forward fuselage. Used by the 8th Air
Force on operational tests over Europe it
required very long run-ins to obtain
accurate target identification.**

4
Champion Fortresses

The operational life of a Fortress depended on the war zone in which the bomber served and the period of that commitment. The deep penetration of German airspace by unescorted B-17s of the 8th Air Force during 1943 brought the heaviest attrition, with survival averaging less than 100 days during one period. The average life of an 8th Air Force B-17 for the whole war period was 215 days, during which it was non-operational for 119 days and undergoing repair or maintenance on 49 days, and on the remaining 47 days it was flying combat missions. In the first year of operations a B-17 was notable if it survived 25 operations in the European Theatre of Operations (ETO). Of the four combat groups commencing operations in the autumn of 1942 with some 150

B-17Fs in total, an equivalent number had been lost by the time the first individual B-17 completed 25 missions in May 1943.

The first Fortress to reach the quarter-century milestone, according to the official 8th Air Force press release at the time, was an aircraft nicknamed *Hell's Angels*. This was an original B-17F of the 358th Bomb Squadron, 303rd Bomb Group, serial number 41-24577, battle letters VK:D, which had commenced its combat career on 17 November 1942 and suffered no aborts — turn-backs for mechanical or personnel failures. The same source gave 14 May 1943 as the date of this achievement, although 303rd Bomb Group records indicate that this may have occurred three days later. Around the same date nine other 8th Air Force B-17Fs completed their 25th mission, of which *Delta Rebel II*, 42-5077, OR:T of 323rd Bomb Squadron, 91st Bomb Group is credited with reaching this goal on 15 May 1943. The

picture is confused because of local interpretations of what constituted a mission completed — a single combat sortie. At some levels a combat sortie was credited even if a bomber had aborted at the enemy coast. Additionally the 8th Air Force Public Relations Office was promoting a documentary called *The Memphis Belle* at this time, which featured a B-17F of that name and its crew who were the first to complete 25 missions and be sent home to the USA from the UK. *The Memphis Belle*, 41-24485, DF:A, completed its 25 missions on 19 May 1943 and due to the publicity accorded it at the time is frequently but incorrectly stated to have been first to reach the 25 mark.

The first 8th Air Force Fortress to complete 50 missions was *Knock-Out Dropper*, a B-17F serial 41-24605, BN:R of 359th Bomb Squadron, 303rd Bomb Group, which reached this total on 16 November 1943. However, during the year taken to reach the half-century

Below:
Hell's Angels with scoreboard showing 41 missions and nine enemy fighter claims.

Above:
Knock-Out Dropper art featured a pipette dispensing bomb-like drops.

mark the bomber had aborted on no less than 12 other missions. *Hell's Angels* of the same group had 47 missions to its credit at this date and still had no aborts to mar its record. After one more mission *Hell's Angels* was sent back to the United States for publicity purposes. (Note: At one time or another there were at least 10 similarly nicknamed B-17s among 8th Air Force units).

Knock-Out Dropper continued on operations and on 27 March 1944 became the first B-17 in the ETO to reach 75 missions completed and was thereafter retired. As far as is known, no 8th Air Force B-17F came near to reaching the next significant milestone, 100 missions, in the course of normal bombing operations. The benefits of electronic supercharger controls were such that the remaining B-17Fs with their hydraulic controls were the principal candidates for retirement by combat groups. Few remained in service by the summer of 1944 and only the odd example soldiered on into the autumn months. The last is believed to have been *Blind Date*, 42-30195, E of 560th Bomb Squadron, 388th Bomb Group, which crashed after taking off for its 67th mission on 7 October 1944. The only 8th Air Force B-17Fs that did pass 100

missions were the few that survived with the Night Leaflet Squadron of which the champion is believed to have been *Miss Mickey Finn*, 42-30656, J6:W, with 151 missions by the end of hostilities.

By the spring of 1944 8th Air Force had a policy whereby news releases would only mention individual bomber record mission totals which had been achieved without incurring a turn-back for mechanical or equipment failure. This arose through the possibility of ground crews being more concerned with collecting a record for their charges than with efficient maintenance. The policy of not giving publicity to record breakers that had aborted was fairly rigidly adhered to, even beyond the end of hostilities. As a result, the first 8th Air Force B-17 to pass 100 missions was never officially acknowledged. The first to reach that figure without suffering an abort is claimed to be *Swamp Fire*, a B-17G 42-32024, WA:L of 524th Bomb Squadron, 379th Bomb Group. To obtain the record this Fortress completed the mission of 2 November 1944 on three engines. In the weeks that followed, an increasing number of Fortresses reached the century in completed combat sorties and by May 1945 B-17 groups that had been in action for a year could boast centenarians, some as many as 10. Adherence to the policy of only allowing completed sorties to count made the supreme 8th

Air Force B-17 champion — announced after hostilities ceased — *Nine O Nine*, B-17G 42-31909, OR:R of 323rd Bomb Squadron, 91st Bomb Group, with 140 missions. Runner up was *Milk Wagon*, B-17G 43-37756, G of 708th Bomb Squadron, 447th Bomb Group, with 128 missions. There were several B-17s that had one or more aborted sorties but with totals in excess of both these figures, of which the highest was the 157 missions of *Ol' Gappy*, B-17G 42-40003, WA:H of 524th Bomb Squadron, 379th Bomb Group. *Ol' Gappy* flew its first mission on 30 January 1944 and its last on 25 April 1944, only having failed to complete one additional mission.

In the Mediterranean Theatre of Operations (MTO) the champions are more obscure. The 12th Air Force B-17Fs flew many tactical missions in support of the ground campaign in North Africa, which often required only brief penetration of hostile airspace, albeit that some targets were heavily defended.

Top right:
Delta Rebel II with 20 missions, 10 enemy fighter claims and pictured with her regular pilot, Lt Charles Cliburn, at Bassingbourn on 6 April 1943.

Right:
Ol' Gappy with 40 missions photographed on 12 June 1944. The motif consisted of topper, gloves and collar with nothing in between.

Below:
Patched and worn *Berlin Sleeper II* with 100 up.

Above:
B-17E 41-2472 with over 200 operational flights. The aircraft symbols are for enemy fighters claimed.

Overall attrition was not so great. For example, in March 1943 the 8th Air Force lost 24 B-17s while the 12th Air Force only two; while both flew a similar number of sorties. As a result North African based B-17Fs amassed missions much more quickly than those flying from England, and several eventually reached the 100 milestone. The first was the *Berlin Sleeper II*, 41-24370 of 342nd Bomb Squadron, 97th Bomb Group, which made its 100th trip on 13 September 1943. This aircraft had flown its first missions from England before the 97th Group moved to Africa. Its final total was 103.

The MTO B-17F with the most missions is believed to be *Fort Alamo II*, 42-29696, with a total of 131. This aircraft flew most of its missions with the 99th Bomb Group and was then transferred to the 483rd Bomb Group.

The 15th Air Force after moving to bases in southern Italy, was committed to the strategic bombing campaign, and

met equally stiff opposition in forays over Germany and Austria to that encountered by the 8th Air Force. The less humid and warmer operating environment in the air, however, saw B-17Fs enduring on operations for a much longer period than in the ETO, and several examples of this model had mission totals in excess of 100. The 15th Air Force engaged in many short-range tactical operations in support of the Allied armies in Italy and the ageing B-17Fs were usually confined to these raids. A number of the Force's B-17Gs also completed more than 100 operations, and the individual aircraft with the highest total is believed to have been *Sweet 17*, 42-32017 of 483rd Bomb Group which was lost in action in its 144th mission — to Almasfuzite, Hungary on 14 March 1945.

The small force of B-17E and F models involved in the war against Japan were withdrawn during the summer of 1943. Some of these aircraft ran up more than

200 missions, but the majority were sea searches. Of these aircraft a B-17E, *Guinea Pig* serial 41-2472, has been credited with flying 212 missions between 22 January 1942 and 5 October 1943. Originally assigned to the 7th Bomb Group in Java, it later served with the 19th Bomb Group in Australia and, after this group left the theatre, finished its days with the 43rd Bomb Group. This aircraft also carried symbols on its nose indicating the destruction of 23 Japanese fighters. This was more an indication of action rather than destruction, and the same applied in other theatres of war. Several 8th and 12th Air Force B-17s were decorated with symbols signifying the destruction of between 10 and 20 enemy aircraft.

Appendix 1

USAAF B-17 Disposition — November 1941 to August 1945

The above table shows the disposition of USAAF B-17s at the end of each month from November 1941 to August 1945. The first column gives the number of new B-17s accepted from factories and includes those that were subsequently delivered to the RAF and US Navy. The second column shows the end of month total of B-17s in USAAF service worldwide and the last two columns the distribution between the continental USA and overseas. From half to two-thirds of the USA monthly figure involves aircraft at modification centres or awaiting overseas delivery. The sharp increase in June and July 1945 is the result of B-17s being returned from Europe after hostilities ceased.

The average cost of a B-17B, C and D for the 1939-41 period was $301,221. B-17Es and B-17Fs of 1942 averaged $258,949. In 1944 B-17Gs averaged $204,370 per unit and the final deliveries in 1945 were reduced to an average cost of $187,742 each. This included the airframe and all equipment installed on the fly-away aircraft at the factory.

	Factory Acceptances	On hand USAAF	On hand USA	On hand Overseas with USAAF
Nov 41	55	145	84	61
Dec 41	93	198	117	81
Jan 42	74	221	107	114
Feb 42	75	261	133	128
Mar 42	85	355	211	144
Apr 42	90	445	281	164
May 42	90	499	312	187
Jun 42	99	535	333	202
Jul 42	107	645	408	237
Aug 42	121	721	393	328
Sep 42	137	830	501	329
Oct 42	150	926	505	421
Nov 42	163	1063	604	459
Dec 42	221	1239	769	470
Jan 43	199	1356	892	464
Feb 43	259	1556	1082	474
Mar 43	286	1765	1148	617
Apr 43	327	2035	1144	891
May 43	345	2265	1175	1090
Jun 43	333	2460	1282	1178
Jul 43	379	2675	1416	1259
Aug 43	383	2874	1643	1231
Sep 43	386	3031	1772	1259
Oct 43	406	3194	1859	1335
Nov 43	426	3270	1752	1518
Dec 43	450	3528	1868	1660
Jan 44	472	3717	1896	1821
Feb 44	488	3836	2038	1798
Mar 44	578	4070	2165	1905
Apr 44	475	4160	2126	2034
May 44	524	4268	2225	2043
Jun 44	508	4428	2359	2069
Jul 44	468	4525	2386	2139
Aug 44	476	4574	2311	2263
Sep 44	422	4552	2067	2485
Oct 44	327	4499	1764	2735
Nov 44	308	4440	1614	2823
Dec 44	306	4419	1533	2886
Jan 45	319	4253	1335	2918
Feb 45	304	4146	1178	2968
Mar 45	307	3972	966	3006
Apr 45	243	3717	880	2837
May 45	179	3654	1023	2631
Jun 45	136	3692	1907	1785
Jul 45	64	3675	2449	1226
Aug 45		3677	2405	1272

Appendix 2

USAAF B-17 Deployment in Theatres of War — November 1941 to August 1945

● **ETO** — European Theatre of Operations covered Western Europe and in this case applies only to B-17s of the 8th Air Force operating from the United Kingdom.

● **MTO** — Mediterranean Theatre of Operations covers B-17s operating from the Middle East (9th Air Force) until November 1942, then North Africa (12th Air Force) until November 1943, and thereafter Italy (15th Air Force).

● **POA** — Pacific Ocean Area covering island groups across the central Pacific where eight B-17 squadrons served with the 7th Air Force — until transferred to the FEAF.

● **FEAF** — Far East Air Forces applied to Australia, New Guinea and the Solomon Islands where B-17s served with the 5th and 13th Air Forces in 16 squadrons at different times.

● **CBI** — China-Burma-India theatre found only a maximum of two B-17 squadrons operating in India and Burma with the 10th Air Force.

● The figures given cover only bomber configured B-17s and not those designated for other purposes such as transport or air-sea rescue. For example, there was an average of 20 B-17Gs converted as airborne lifeboat carriers and for special transports with the 20th Air Force in the Marianas Islands during the summer of 1945. Neither do the figures include second-line aircraft used for training and communications work. An average 120 war-weary B-17s were in hand for such duties during the period May 1944-May 1945.

● **ALASKA** — The 11th Air Force engaged in operations against the Japanese in the Aleutian Islands and had a single B-17 squadron for some months.

	ETO	MTO	POA	FEAF	CBI	ALASKA
Nov 41			12	35		
Dec 41			42	14		
Jan 42			39	27	3	
Feb 42			42	23	8	
Mar 42			32	27	10	1
Apr 42			32	45	12	1
May 42			57	51	19	1
Jun 42			73	67	19	8
Jul 42	44	10	36	99	12	6
Aug 42	104	10	36	108	8	5
Sep 42	144	11	23	124	10	11
Oct 42	234	11	2	119	10	11
Nov 42	108	64	1	119	10	11
Dec 42	178	68	1	110	10	11
Jan 43	175	118	1	98	10	10
Feb 43	186	142	1	92	10	10
Mar 43	229	167	1	85	10	5
Apr 43	502	195	1	81	10	4
May 43	599	229	1	76	4	4
Jun 43	783	269	1	70	4	5
Jul 43	820	314	1	65	2	5
Aug 43	786	338	1	64	2	6
Sep 43	835	313	1	58	2	6
Oct 43	907	298			1	2
Nov 43	1166	268			1	
Dec 43	1302	289				
Jan 44	1341	309				
Feb 44	1412	289				
Mar 44	1487	397				
Apr 44	1492	368				
May 44	1502	361				
Jun 44	1471	315				
Jul 44	1695	316				
Aug 44	1829	366				
Sep 44	1927	407				
Oct 44	2143	476				
Nov 44	2123	476				
Dec 44	2168	509				
Jan 45	2125	538				
Feb 45	2269	521				
Mar 45	2367	524				
Apr 45	2291	497				
May 45	1988	529				
Jun 45	1147	457				
Jul 45	787	377				
Aug 45	780	343				